Silver's City

by Fra McCartney

Printed in 2021 by Shanway Press, 15 Crumlin Road, Belfast BT14 6AA

ISBN: 978-1-910044-31-5

I would like to thank everyone who helped me
in putting this book together.
My two sisters – Bernadette and Marian; Sean McErlean,
Joe McCullough, Pat Rooney and Dominic Quinn.

This book is dedicated to
all the great people of Belfast

I was born in Belfast into a family of 11 children in 1949 when the world was starting to change dramatically. I started school when I was four years old and so began an adventure of the love for horses, horse dealers, and the ordinary man or woman who made good in this great city or in far-off distant lands they emigrated to.

My days in the merchant navy took me to many countries. It was exciting, but if I was standing in Sydney Harbour or Miami Beach they could never match the city that I loved, Belfast. I've always thought about writing about this great city, but then everyone has written a book about Belfast, so I decided to write a book about the characters rather than the city.

When writing this book it metamorphosed into a story about redemption and in some way, this is a story about redemption of the characters whom may have fallen from grace but in most people's eyes were great people.

In some way every writer. so they say, writes themselves into anything they work on, so I'm in there somewhere, perhaps more than I think. But it has given me great pleasure writing this book about the people, places, and things that I love; and that is Belfast and my redemption. The *raison d'etre* for this book is my love of Belfast.

Fra McCartney, 2021

Once upon a time in Belfast there was Silver

Chapter 1

I was about ten years old at the time and it was just before Christmas when my father asked me would I like to go with him to the Belfast market to purchase a turkey for our family's Christmas dinner. I thought for a minute, then I looked at my Da and I said to myself, "I've nothing better to do, so why not?"

As we walked along Servia Street in the Falls Road district of west Belfast, I wondered what the markets would be like as I'd never been there before. My mind wondered and I could visualise all the market traders, farmers, horse dealers and chicken sellers, reminiscent of a farmyard in the city. We had cousins who owned a farm in Randalstown where my grandfather had a wee country house and I had visited it a few times. As we approached Oxford Street I couldn't help but notice that Belfast city centre was different from what I had imagined. One that I'd never seen before and I was fascinated by it all. Large buildings to each side of me, and lots of people busying themselves, going about their lives at a very fast pace. It was all very new to me and I felt as if I was in America, the America I had only seen in films in the Clonard picture house.

Then my da and me entered the arena: a large cobbled stone square yard with lorries, vans, horses and traps, handcarts, and people calling out to each other in what was then a strange language to me. Men where slapping hands which I found out later was the conclusion of a deal, a gentleman's agreement, no papers, no receipt, just a spit on the hand and a generous slap of hands, the deal was done. I was amazed to say the least.

As my eyes panned around this mecca of traders, one person stood out among the ladies selling fruit and vegetables and men, young and old who were jogging the odd horse up and down the square, hoping to catch the eye of a buyer. Or as they say, have a deal and end with the slap of the hands. A bull of a man was leaning against the shafts of a horse and cart, and he stood out like a beacon. He was smoking a cigarette and holding his ash plant, a large stick used by cattle drovers to steer cattle into their pens; he was different in so many ways to the others. He was as broad as he was tall, with flaxen hair; his buffers knot perched under his chin, he was someone special. He was wearing a nice Ulster coat sometimes called a Crombie and tan or yellow boots.

A big fat man was selling chickens and turkeys from the back of his van and

I watched as my father moved his right hand every now and then. I found out later he was making a bid for a turkey, but all to no avail. I pulled him on his arm and asked him as I pointed.

"Who's that da?"

He paused for a moment and looked at me.

"Just the man I'm looking for. That's Paddy Joe McKee".

As I tripped after my da weaving among the crowd and the numerous horses and carts I was aware then that my da knew the man I had being gazing at. They both shook hands and my da asked Paddy would he bid for a turkey for him, about a sixteen pounder would do the job. Paddy moved away from his position and walked closer to the auction put his hand up twice and low and behold he was handed a turkey. As he walked back to my da and me he said, "That's fifty bob Robert".

As my da was paying him, he asked how much Paddy had to get for doing the deal. He replied, "For God sakes Robert, we're friends. You owe me nothing. You can buy me a drink the next time we meet." I was amazed.

Then someone shouted "Silver!" and Paddy Joe looked up.

"Have to go Robert. Is this your son?" My da nodded. Paddy took a half crown from his pocket and handed it to me. "Don't spend that all in the one shop," as he laughed, shook hands again with my da and left. I was confused because my da was calling him Paddy and someone else was calling him Silver and he responded to that name as well.

"Da," I asked, "who is that man?"

"That's the one and only Silver McKee son," he replied.

I took my hand out of my pocket. It was firmly clasped on my half crown and I said to myself, "Silver McKee gave me that." This was the man I had heard the elder fellows at the street corner talk about. Silver McKee, the hardest man in all Ireland. He supposedly fought any man who got in his way and he had just given me a half crown. And so started my fascination for the man who stood out from all the others, a giant in many ways, the stuff of dreams. He was also the man that folklore implied to be the hardest street fighter in the world, according to a Readers Digest I read in the dentists as I awaited for my first tooth to be pulled?

* * *

About six months later as I was dandering down town trying to sell my last Belfast Telegraphs I spied Silver McKee and his wife-walking arm in arm up the town, like two film stars of the day. Probably on their way to the pictures or a quiet drink somewhere. As he walked up Howard Street a big hard-nosed Gypsy stepped out of a public house and looked up and down the street. Silver then began briskly walking up the street as his poor wife Mary tried hard to keep up with him. She abruptly stopped and asked him what was wrong. Silver pointed back down the street.

"Him, he's a bogey," That was the name given to a nuisance or someone he didn't want to meet. The Gypsy, I found out later was called Bronco Doyle. He was rubbing his chin, which looked like leather. Rough, weather-beaten with scars all over it, he would scare the life out of lesser mortals.

He roared up the street, "Sheeps head! Sheeps head!" He roared again as Silver ignored him and hurried along.

"Sheeps head, you're a coward. You live on your name. I'm Bronco Doyle and I'm the man, I'll fight any man for fifty pounds!"

Silver stops and after a few words with his wife and a bit of pulling and hauling he kisses her on the cheek, unbuttons his trademark yellow Crombie coat and walks down the street towards Bronco.

By this time a crowd having heard all the commotion had gathered outside the pub. Bronco was roaring and there were people arguing with each other. One of the men, Brendan Bell, ran into the pub and returned with a beer box and he stood on it.

"I'll take three to one Silver, five to two the gypsy king!"

The crowd then moved into a small side street as Silver handed his coat to a friend of his, Croaky McNally. He then dipped into his pocket and counts twenty-five pounds out, and throws it on the ground. Bronco who is jumping about like a man possessed, roaring and shouting, throws his twenty-five pounds on the road and roars.

"I've another twenty-five quid if any man is game enough to take the bet!"

Brendan Bell gets down from his box, counts out twenty-five pounds, and throws it on the ground and declares, "I'm backing Silver!" The barman who is among the crowd walks forward, lifts the money and declares that he would referee the fight and hold the money until a winner is declared.

"I'm going kill you, McKee !" cries Bronco.

"I'll take three to one Silver and you can have any price Doyle!" roars Bell as he mounts his rostrum. Just then the crowd surges towards Brendan Bell and he shouts, "Don't worry you will all get on! Three to one Bronco: four to one on Silver!"

After he takes all the bets Brendan gets down off his box and shouts to the crowd to form a ring.

"Now men keep it clean, shake hands and come out fighting!" says the referee.

As Silver puts his hand out to shake Bronco's hand, Bronco throws a big Judas punch and connects with Silver's jaw. As he goes down on one knee Bronco tries to kick him in the head. As Silver is down on one knee trying to get his breath back the crowd roar and Brendan jumps in the middle of the fighters. The referee pushes Brendan out of the way.

Brendan is a small man but full of energy and as strong as a bull: "None of that here,

Bronco this is Belfast!" Bronco also throws Brendan out of his way like a rag doll and this gives Silver enough time to get up on his feet again.

"There's no need for you now," says Silver to the referee, "this will be over in a few minutes." Silver throws a left hand, which lands on Broncos chin but he keeps coming forward. Silver moves down to his ribs and gives him a left and a right and then an upper cut and Bronco falls to the ground.

The crowd is chanting "Silver! Silver! Silver!" as Bronco is being sick all over himself. Silver goes to get his coat. Suddenly someone throws a machete on the road beside Bronco and he grabs it and starts attacking Silver. Silver is looking for something to protect himself but to no avail.

He throws his coat over Bronco's arm to block the machete. As Bronco gets tangled up with Silver's coat, it gives Silver time to protect himself from the machete. He then lifts Brendan's wooden box and uses it as a shield as Bronco hacks at Silver in a wild frenzy. Bronco makes a mad slash at Silver and the machete gets caught in the box and Silver steps out, gives Bronco two digs to the chin and a haymaker of a punch to the ribs. It's all over. Bronco is down and out but Silver walks over, gets astride him and pounds his ribs for a few minutes.

"I've never done that on a man before, but any man who uses a weapon on me had better be prepared. I'll break him in half!" Silver tells the crowd. Silver gets his fifty pounds and Brendan also gives him a fistful of money.

"Great job Silver, a great job, now lets go and get a drink. It's thirsty work making a book and watching you fight." Just then the barman walks out with a bucket of water and throws it over Bronco who gets up and growls.

"I'll be back!" cries Bronco, to which Brendan replies, "You better bring an army with you the next time!" Silver tidies himself up and Brendan, Croaky, and himself retire to the pub. Just then the police arrive and everyone quickly disperses in all directions. Silver is standing at the bar in the Black Bull public house and he has the crowd in raptures.

"Every gypsy in Ireland will want to fight me now. I'll have to keep my head down." The bar bursts into laughter. As I walk into the hall of the pub I put my head in the door and peek into the public bar. A sawdust-strewn place with mirrors and glass everywhere, I had never seen anything like it. Men drinking pints of Guinness, glasses of whiskey, wine, and beer; it was like a carnival with the entire atmosphere that goes with it. Women are singing at the top of their voices and men are queuing up to buy Silver a drink. I meekly walked over to Silver and stood looking at him. I was amazed. I was standing beside my hero and from that day I wanted to emulate Silver. And so started my quest to become the man, the Belfast man.

Chapter 2

A few days later Silver is sitting at the table eating his dinner when Mary walks into the living room and throws the daily newspaper in front of him. "Well that's the end of that. What are you going to do now for work, Mr. Markets?"

"What are you on about woman?"

"Read that and then you will know, but in a way it may be a good thing. I always wanted to move out of this place and live up the country in a house with a wee garden, a bit like my mothers house."

Silver lifts the newspaper and the headlines read:

BELFAST MARKETS TO BE CLEARED FOR REDEVELOPMENT .

Silver throws the paper on the table. "Over my dead body!" he says in a rage.

"I thought you'd say that, but one man can't stand in the way of change, not you Paddy or any of your cronies," Mary utters sarcastically.

"We'll see about that." Silver drinks the rest of his tea, gets up and puts on his coat and tries to kiss Mary on the cheek. Mary turns away.

"I suppose that's another excuse to go around to the Black Bull and tell everyone what your going to do to stop this all happening. Not that you ever needed an excuse to go to that den of iniquity."

"I'm not going to the pub; I'm going to see a couple of my big shot friends, as you call them.

They owe me little favours and its time I was calling them in."

"Look Paddy, can you not sit in for just one night. The Black Bull will be there when you're not there. You can be sure of that."

Silver pushes by Mary, walks out the door and heads up the street. Just as Mary had predicted Silver heads into the pub and forgets all the promises he had made to her.

As Silver opens the door he is met by some of the drovers that work for him all waving newspapers at him and shouting and cursing. It is complete bedlam.

"Give me a glass of whiskey, a bottle of stout and a glass of water!" he calls to the barman. Croaky McNally stands beside Silver and lets him get a drink of the whiskey and then asks him what they were to do if this all happens. He opens the newspaper and points to the headlines and utters, "It can't be true. I've read it. Bad news if there's any truth to it."

"But it can't be true," says Silver. "Look, give me a few minutes to settle and think for God's sake will you. Let me know this whiskey's mine."

The bar is buzzing and groups of men are forming around each table locked in deep conversation. Silver walks into the middle of the bar like a matador and calls for order. "Listen lads. Does anyone really know if this is true?"

A young man appears from the back of the crowd and asks Silver, "Can I speak Mister?" "Who the hell are you? Sit down and be quiet!" comes a roar from the crowd.

"Who are you anyway son? This is important business we're discussing and I've no time for any nonsense?"

"My name is John Rodgers and I work in the Belfast Planning Office, up the street in the
City Hall and I have seen the out-line plans."

Silver calls for order. John is dressed very conservatively and stands out like a duck out of water among the cattlemen. The drovers start cat calling him. Silver calls for order again. Silence falls except for the chink of glasses. You could hear a pin drop.

"I have come here tonight because I was born in the market and I had a good idea that Paddy would be here."

"Who is he?" someone in the crowd shouts, "throw him out!"

"My father was killed in Allams sale yard by a bull, so I'm as much a market man as anyone of youse. Don't let the dress attire fool you, and no, I don't wear brown dealer boots but I thought it my duty to come here and inform you all, especially Silver who was my fathers friend. I have seen the plans and it's happening, I can assure you all of that. "

Silver grabs John by the arm. "Are you big John's son? I stood for you when you were christened in St. Malachy's. My godson? It's a small world. How's your wee ma Lily doing?"

A softness comes over Silver but he hides it by pulling his handkerchief out of his pocket and rubs his face with it. Suddenly everyone in the bar has surrounded John and Silver as they ask questions and hear tales of his father, a well-known drover who got killed by a charging bull, that Silver actually knocked out with a single blow after the attack. Silver pushes everyone back and takes John into a cubicle usually the preserve of married or courting couples. He hails Croaky and another big drover called Lofty and they go into the cubicle. Silver holds court.

"What can we do John?"

"Well, Paddy, if I was one of you, a drover I mean, I'd be either looking for a new job, or joining, or forming a trade union."

Croaky laughs, "A trade union? Are you joking? It's sometimes hard enough to earn a week's wages never mind paying into a trade union."

"Let the lad speak." says Silver.

"You have just answered your own dilemma; if you were members of a trade union you could then have some leverage and power but if not you have no strength."

"Look son, if the farmers didn't give us the odd bung, we wouldn't be able to come in here for the odd bottle of stout at night."

"I think the odd bottle of stout is an understatement but that's beside the point," says John. Lofty asks, "Can I have a word?"

"Surely go ahead."

"I knew your father well, John, and he was a very smart and clever man and the funny thing about it, he always wanted us to join the Transport Workers Union and I want to hear all you have to say."

"I think Lofty is right. We can listen Croaky and if we like what he has to say well the jobs a good'n and if we don't we can try something else."

As young John explains to a very attentive Silver and Big Lofty, Croaky is no more interested than the man in the moon about trade unions and going on strike.

"I've six kids," cries Croaky.

"So have I," adds Lofty, "it's alright for you, Paddy Joe, you've none. I need my wages every week."

"I have never claimed the dole in my life and I'm not starting now," says Silver.

Croaky gets up, lifts his glass of stout and walks out of the snug and says,

"Among you be it, but count me out."

Lofty gets up to call Croaky back but Silver tells him to sit down and at least listen to the lad. John explains that he knows a man up the Shankill Road called Trevor Wilson whom, although he's from the Shankill, is a delegate in the Irish Transport and General Workers Union and he's the man they need to see.

Lofty asks, "How are we supposed to find him? We don't know many up the 'heel and ankle' and the ones we know are not trade union men."

Silver looks at John, straight in the face. "Are you sure this man would help us?"

"As sure as the priest said mass on Sunday. Trevor is your man and he doesn't care where you're from. He's a union man through and through."

Silver calls the barman. "Harry! Phone me a taxi from Silver Cabs. I'm going up the Shankill to find this man and then all the talking will be over. Lofty, I don't want you to come up with me but John, I'd like you to come with me to explain the situation."

"But mister I'm only married and if I'm not home for my dinner in half an hour there'll be a search party out looking for me." Silver orders a large Jamesons and tells Lofty and John that he has a pal up there and if anyone can help me find what's his name, he's the man.

"Who's that Paddy?" asks Lofty.

"Stormy Weatherall. We have had a couple of run ins, but he's a decent enough fellow and he will find what's his name."

"Trevor Wilson," says John.

"Write that down because as sure as there's an eye in a buck goat, I'll forget it." John tears a cigarette packet in halves and writes it down.

"If you meet him, tell him I recommended him. He's a nice man and very helpful. Would you not be as well leaving it till tomorrow morning, Silver? It's pitch black outside; leave it for a day or two."

After a few more glasses of whiskey a man puts his head into the bar and shouts "Taxi for McKee.!"

Silver stands up, puts his head out of the snug, "That's me. I'll be with you in a minute." "Are you sure you don't want company, Silver?" cries Lofty.

"No I never go team handed. I go alone and I wouldn't ask any man to do what I wouldn't or couldn't do myself."

"For gods sake your half watered," says Lofty.

"I never felt better in my life. I'm away. I'll see you in the morning, Lofty and don't have me to come round to get you out of bed." Silver walks out the door and Croaky makes his way down to Lofty.

"Where's he away to?"

"He's away up the Shankill to see Stormy Weatherall," says Lofty.

"And you let him go to fight a man in that state?" cries Croaky.

"He's not away to fight him Mister McNally, he's away to try and find a man and he's meeting Mister Weatherall to find out where the man lives," says John.

" Listen son your talking crap. I've heard it all before. Silver has been itching for this for years. It's going to turn into a fight you mark my words."

Meanwhile Silver is in the front passenger seat of the taxi and he starts talking to the driver.

"What bar does Stormy drink in now? Have you any idea?"

"I would bet he's in the Rex. That's his watering hole."

"Why? Do you know him? He's a bit of a hard man you know. Some say he knocked out three men in one fight."

"I've heard all them rumors but I can assure you son, he won't be knocking this man out."

The taxi driver laughs. "Sure you're half drunk mister. In your state you couldn't pull the tail out of a sweetie mouse."

Silver lifts his head from between his legs and looks at the driver. "Do you know me son?"

"No. All I know is your name is McKee but I do know Stormy. He lives beside me up the Shankill and no one, and I mean no one, talks back to him."

The taxi pulls up at the Rex. "That's eight-shillings, Mister." Silver hands him a ten bob note, telling him to keep the change.

"That's a tip from your uncle Silver." The taxi driver looks at him and tries to remonstrate with him to get back in the car. He now knows who he is and knows there's going to be a row.

"Look Silver get back in. I will run you back to the Black Bull. If you go in there, Stormy will beat the crap out of you. Sure everyone knows you two hate each other."

" That's wrong son, I never hated anyone in my life and I'm not here to fight."

Silver shrugs his shoulders and walks into the Rex and orders a large Jameson. You could hear a pin drop as Silver swaggers down the bar.

"Look what the wind blew in!" cries the barman, "Patrick Joseph McKee!"

The door of the pub opens and in peeps the taxi driver. He runs out again and to every one that passes on the busy Shankill Road he tells them that a big fight is about to take place between Silver McKee and Stormy. Before long a crowd has gathered outside the Rex as the news has travelled like wildfire around the Shankill. There are women who have just come out of their homes with scarfs on and rollers in their hair, young lads and girls, it is like a jamboree. Back inside the bar and Silver is now talking to Stormy as he searches his pockets for the lump of paper with Trevor's name on it, which now escapes drunken Silver.

"So you're up here to fight me. You're pretending you're here to find some one and you don't even know his name. I'd advise you to go on back to the house and sober up. Come back when you've sobered up and I will have a fair go at you, any time that suits you or any of your cronies."

Silver lifts his glass, drinks the whiskey and looks at the glass then sets it on the bar upside down.

"Here! We'll have none of that here. Take yourself out before you get carried out!" shouts the barman. Silver turns and looks at a now crowded bar and says,"who's going to make me?"

Stormy walks over and grabs Silver by the lapels. Stormy is also built like a bull but a little taller than Silver. "I'm going to give you a bye ball, Paddy, because I know you. But don't be coming back here throwing your weight around. This is my road and don't you forget it. You stick to cow walloping in the market. Now I advise you to go."

Silver pulls Stormy's hands of his lapels and beckons him outside and Stormy follows. As Silver walks out the front door there is literally hundreds on the street baying for his blood. Silver throws off his coat and squares up to Stormy who takes off his coat reluctantly and the two men get stuck in. Suddenly the fight becomes a melee and its like Silver is fighting the whole of the Shankill. Women are pulling his hair and the odd boot is coming in from all angles. Stormy grabs Silver by the neck and pulls him down the street and calls the taxi driver who he knows, and tells him to get his taxi quickly. The taxi driver runs down the street, gets into his taxi and drives up to the corner where Stormy and Silver are wrestling and Stormy pushes Silver into the back seat and he gets in the front beside the driver.

"Look Paddy, you've no chance tonight and probably never had but that's beside the point.

We're going for a drink in the Naval Club. Drive us down to the Naval Club, driver and sharpish. That crowd wants this mans blood." The driver takes off with Stormy and Silver and drives down to the Naval Club where both men get out and Stormy helps Silver who is reluctant to go in.

Chapter 3

The next morning Silver comes down the stairs and cracks a joke to Mary who is definitely not interested in his funny remarks. Silver walks down to the scullery and throws some water on his face and looks in the mirror. His face is covered in scratches and small cuts and there's blood in his hair. He turns the water tap on full force and sticks his head under it for a few minutes and calls out to Mary to get him a towel. Mary brings the towel in and reminds him that he should have got the towel before he started to wash his hair. She then asks him where he had been the night before.

"Well, Mary," he says, "I went up the Shankill to see a man and we had a few drinks and one thing led to another. There was a bit of a row but nothing serious and I came on home."

"Who where you fighting with this time?"

"I fell out with a fellow called Stormy Weatherall but we finished up the best of friends and that's the way it should be."

"By the look of your face, you'd think you where fighting a crowd of alley cats."Silver laughs as he tries to make light of the subject but Mary is having none of it.

"I'm warning you Paddy Joe. If the fighting doesn't stop I'm leaving you and I mean it."

"Catch yourself on Mary, sure where would you go?" Mary steps back as Silver finishes drying his hair.

"I'm not too old yet to start a new life without being described as Silver's wife and every night not knowing whether you're going to come home dead or alive."

Silver chuckles, "It would take some man to kill me," he laughs, "it would take some man." Silver ponders for a minute or so... "Look, I promise you Mary, I won't start another fight; honest I won't fight again as long as I live."

"Ha, ha, ha. You wont start another fight but some of your cronies will and when trouble comes knocking on our door there's none of them in sight. You're a mug Paddy and the sooner you realise that, the sooner you will get on in this life. We have our own family to contend with not half the market area."

Silver looks around him and snaps, "is there anyone else here that I don't know about because the last time I looked our family was you and me."

"Well. that's going to change and when that day comes you had better change as well, or I will leave this house for good."

"Now take it easy, Mary, you're getting on like someone not wise."

"Do you want to know something, Big Silver McKee? You haven't the brains you were born with."

Silver starts combing his long golden locks and looks at Mary with scorn. "Ach! woman, you don't know what you're talking about"

"Maybe I do and maybe I don't, but the doctor knows and I think he's more brains than the two of us put together."

Silver sits motionless for a minute and jumps up. "Are you sick Mary?"

"Yes, sick sore and tired of being married to a single man with no consideration for me or anyone else for that matter. All you think of is your big shot friends who used and abused you. Not one of them ever calls to say do you need anything except big Lofty. Not even that Croaky one. Ach! What's the use?"

"Your heads away with it and nothing I'm going to say will change you."

"Well your head will be away when October comes."

"Why? What's happening then may I ask? Is it your birthday or did I forget something?"

"I'm having a baby you big idiot."

Silver jumps up, "you're what?"

"I'm having our baby."

Silver grabs Mary and hugs and kisses her. "Are you sure?"

"Well, as I said the doctor knows better than me. The 16th of October. I will have that baby you are always going on about."

Silver does a bit of a jig across the floor and grabs Mary and waltzes her up and down the kitchen floor.

"That's it, you're going to see a new man. I promise you, I will stop drinking and no more fighting. I promise you Mary as sure as the there's a moon in the sky. Now make me a cup of tea I will get breakfast in the ITL café. Can't wait to tell all the lads I'm going be a Da." Mary walks out into the scullery and a tear is running down Silver's face. He searches for his handkerchief frantically and wipes his eyes as Mary hands him the cup of tea.

"What's wrong? Something in your eyes?"

"No Mary, it's that old hay fever playing up." Silver couldn't admit that he had shed a tear of joy and Mary knew it.

"Funny thing about that hay fever you have. You've worked in the Markets all your life round in Allams, with cows and horses, feeding them, bedding them and it never bothered you before."

"Ach! Woman you've always an answer."

"Well I didn't lick it of the stones in the street. It's time you were away. I need to tidy this house up and please try and come back sober.

"Didn't I tell you I was stopping the drink. Well, what I mean is, I'm cutting down on it?"

"There's as much chance of you stopping drinking as the man in the moon falling out of the sky."

Silver gets up, puts on his coat and gives Mary a kiss on the cheek. Then all of a sudden he remembers he's to meet Trevor at the big clock at ten o'clock. "What time is it Mary?

"There's the clock on the fireplace. Are you blind or are you just happy for me doing everything for you?"

"Jesus! It's half nine. I may get my skates on. See you at tea time Mrs. What you making anyway?

"Bee's knees and chickens ankles. What do you think I'm making. It's Tuesday and that means stew?"

Silver grabs the handle of the door and looks at Mary. "You know I'm fond of you Mary and I love you."

"Get out before I hit you with this brush Paddy."

Silver walks out and closes the door behind him and doddles off down the street with a spring in his step.

* * *

The first person he meets is his right hand man Croaky.

"Look Croaky, can you run the show this morning? I'm off to see that man about starting a union. You'll be the only member; none of the gang is interested but go you on. I will get everyone to work. If Big McCausland is there tell him I need to talk to him." "What do you want to see him about?" asks Croaky.

"He owes me a turn big time and I need that turn now. We all need it and he's the man can sort it out, you can bet on it. By the way I'm going to be a Da."

Croaky pauses for a moment, "Well, if you're going to be a dad you'd better change your ways."

"You sound just like my wife." Silver walks off down the street and as he reaches the bottom of the street Croaky shouts, "To hell with you and your effing trade union!"

Silver arrives at the big clock and spies a small man fitting the description of Trevor. "Hello there Trevor! I'm Paddy. Where can we go for a quiet chat?"

The man replies, "if you don't take your self off I'll call the police." Just then Trevor walks over to Silver who is remonstrating with the man.

Trevor introduces himself. "Hello Silver. I'm Trevor. Nice to meet you."

"Am I glad to see you? This gaunch was going to call the cops on me. What did he think I was looking?"

"Well we are standing at the Big Clock and there's Dubarry's just across the road and you know what this town is like."

The man apologises to him and asks, "Are you Silver McKee?"

"Yes, who did you think I was, the man from Laramie?" The man apologies profusely as he backs off and then turns on his heels and runs down the street.

Trevor asks, "What was that all about?"

"I don't know."

The big clock strikes ten o'clock and Silver looks up and beckons Trevor to follow him as they walk over to Peters bar in Waring Street. They enter the bar just as Peter the owner is opening he door. "Morning Paddy."

"Morning Peter, can you get me a bottle and a halfun. What will you have Trevor?"

"Would a cup of tea be out of the question?" Peter laughs at Silver, "Where did you get him? Not one of your usual cronies."

"We're going over to the corner here and if you can help it, if any nuisances come in, please for God's sake keep them away from us. I've had enough to do me a lifetime this morning. A bottle of stout and a halfun of whiskey for me, Peter, and a wee drop of water. And a cup of tea for the gentleman."

"Coming up, Paddy."

Silver and Trevor sit under the window as the sunrays light up the bar.

Trevor asks, "What can I do to help you? But before you answer can we clear something up first? Is it Silver or Paddy I'm a bit confused?"

"Call me what ever you want as long as you don't call me too early in the morning," laughs Silver.

"No, I'm serious. What is your name?"

"My name is Patrick Joseph McKee but my friends call me Paddy."

"Now that we have that out of the way can you now tell me how I can help you, if I can?" "Well it's a simple as this..."

"Excuse me, Silver, a bottle of Guinness and a nice glass of whiskey and a cup of tea for your friend." Silver and Trevor both go to their respective pockets to pay for the drinks but Peter waves his hands and refuses to take the money. "That's on the house. I owe you one for stopping that row last week. I thought them young guys where going to wreck the place. You shouldn't have bothered, Peter, I was only doing the right thing and sure no one was hurt."

Peter laughed, "I never saw the likes of it. You took your coat off and they run out the front door leaving their drinks and never came back."

Trevor takes a drink of his tea and again asks Silver what it is he can do for him. "As you know Trevor, the Markets is supposedly going to get demolished and we have to protect our jobs."

"It just won't be Allams sale-yard, you know. You have the abattoir and the fish market. Then the fruit and vegetables and that's the whole shebang. So if they're going to demolish the place they will have to relocate. So what's the problem?"

"What do you mean relocate?"

"I mean move elsewhere, maybe up the road or somewhere more convenient."

"There's nowhere more convenient than where it is and what you don't understand, Trevor, it's the life blood of the market area. Just imagine the Rope Works, or the Shipyard was to relocate, what would the people from the Newtownards Road do?"

Trevor scratches his head, "I suppose you have a point but if they move and offer to keep your jobs opened you haven't a leg to stand on."

"So what was young John Rodgers on about when he said you could help us start a union?

"First things first, Paddy. You don't start a union. You join one. That's already going strong and in your case that would be the Irish Transport and General Workers Union." Trevor puts his hand into his inside pocket and pulls out a small card and waves it at Silver.

"What's that?" asks Silver flippantly, "a magic wand." Silver laughs.

"That my friend is the strongest thing a workingman can carry. That's my membership of the Boilermakers Union and without it I can't get a job. Better still no one can take my job if he doesn't carry one of these."

Silver reaches out his hand and Trevor hands him the card and Silver looks at it.

"That wee bit of cardboard entitles you to all that. Sure you could get one of them printed anywhere."

"I suppose you could but without the Union behind you it's useless." Silver calls another whiskey and a cup of tea and startles Peter who is lying on his elbows listening to every word of the conversation.

"Yes, Paddy two minutes."

"That Peter is a wise old fox. He misses nothing you know; he can hear the grass grow."

"Yes," says Trevor, "it takes a wise man to act the fool. Fool!" says Trevor; "He owns the place. Some fool. It's like someone told me if you're going to the country looking a fool..." Silver interrupts... "be sure to bring one with you."

Both men laugh. Peter walks over and sets the drinks on the table and Silver hands him some money.

"You know, I couldn't help overhear your conversation there and believe me, Trevor is one hundred percent right. No union, no clout. Even the barmen have a union now. Bloody nuisance but I have to put up with it." Peter moves into the company and sits down with Trevor and Silver and asks do they mind if he joins in the conversation. Trevor tells Peter that it's Paddy's business and its up to him. Silver lashes the whiskey into him and tells Peter it's no problem but he needs another halfun. Peter jumps up and brings down a whiskey like lightening, afraid of missing some of the conversation.

"All I can tell you is not to try and start a Mickey Mouse union but to join one. There are drovers down in Dublin and I'm sure they are all members of the Transport and General."

"So how do we join?"

"Get someone who is level headed and get him to go to their office and have a word with them and get applications forms for anyone who wants to join."

"Well, I won't look any further. No, not me Silver. I've this bar to run. In fact there's a couple of customers coming in. I'll have to leave you and serve them."

"I wasn't referring to you Peter. I was referring to Trevor - he's the man. He has a good way about him; softly spoken and better still, knows what he's talking about. Now you run on and get them boys a drink and bring me another whiskey."

"No tea for me, I'm leaving."

"So will you do it for us Trevor?"

"No. I won't do it for youse. I will do it for you and you never know when I may need a turn from you."

Silver laughs, "Not so slow, Trevor." Trevor takes a cigarette packet out of his pocket and takes a pen out of his inside pocket and starts writing and hands it to Silver.

"When you are ready phone that number and I will meet you again for the next move but let me tell you now. If I do this for you Paddy it's out of respect and the fact I'm a union man. Doesn't matter to me where anyone's from but the union is my life's blood, so please don't mess me around."

"What pub is that?" Silver asks, as he looks at the telephone number?

"That's my home number. One of the perks of being off the drink for a while."

Silver scratches his head as Trevor gets up shakes hands with him and bids him good day. Trevor walks over to Peter at the bar and hands him his empty cup and thanks him. Peter says to Trevor, "Are you a friend of Bill W?" Trevor looks at him a bit surprised and answers, "Yes. Ten years.

How about you?"

"I've only joined a couple of weeks ago."

"Well then, hopefully we will be seeing a lot of each other in the future." Trevor bids Peter good luck and walks out the door. Silver gets up and walks over to Peter and asks, "What was that all about?"

"He attends a place I go to, like a union meeting."

"He seems a sound man. What do you think?"

"What do I think, Silver? I think on first impressions, he's a gentleman."

Silver orders another whiskey and takes a seat at the bar. "Looks like you're here for the day."

"Looks like it. I've nothing better to do. I'm sure everything will be all right. Sure Croaky is looking after things today."

* * *

The next morning Silver walks into the auction ring and calls out to Croaky who walks over to him. "What is it now? I'm in a hurry. I have to get these cattle labelled in order for the ring."

"So you think sticking labels on a cow's arse is more important than what I have to say."

"Well if you had have been here yesterday, you may have known there's big trouble brewing, but sure you were away meeting Trevor, whoever the fuck he is, about some dopey union?

"Have you something you want to get off your chest, McNally? Maybe you've forgotten who's the boss here and I mean just in case you've forgot, I'm the boss here. I give the orders; I don't take them, from you or anyone else for that matter."

"Look Paddy. This is falling apart in front of your eyes and all you want to do is form a union." Croaky turns to walk away and calls out, "and by the way Mary was here looking for you yesterday but then you would have known that if you where at home last night."

"I got caught up in a session last night and finished up in a friend's house and kipped down on the settee."

"You can tell me anything you want. It doesn't really matter but I think by the sound of Mary she's had enough and I'm not far behind her."

"What do you mean?" asks Silver?

"I think she's away up to her mothers and if this keeps going the way it is,

I'll be looking for a new boss."Croaky walks away towards the auction ring and starts shouting at his workers."Hurry up! The auctioneer is ready to start selling cattle. Get them labels stuck on. You'd think you were playing cards. Come on hurry it up!" Silver walks into the auction room and goes straight to the office and walks in.

"What's happening today? How many head have we up today, James?"

"One hundred and sixty but one of our biggest buyers is among the missing so we're in for a hard time today. Prices will be down, in fact I predict a bad sale."

"Who you talking about James?"

"Big McCausland, have you not heard. He's gone missing and so has his son."

"Where has he gone? To the free state for a holiday or is there any big fairs on this week down there?"

"He's gone missing because he didn't pay for last month's cattle. All the cheques have bounced, the whole way from here to Dublin. There's going to be trouble over it Paddy and mark my word, I don't want it knocking on my door or this business. We only sell them for the commission. The rest is between Big Billy McCausland and the farmers."

Silver puts his elbows on the counter and puts his head in his hands. "Have you anything there, James? I was sick coming in this morning. I'm a lot sicker now."

James pulls open the drawer in his desk and produces a half full bottle of whiskey and a glass. He pours a large glass and Silver reaches out but James drinks it in one go, stands up gives a shake and hands Silver the rest of the whiskey. He tells him, "I needed that."

"You can finish the rest. You'll probably need it before the day is over."

Silver pours out the whiskey and with his hand trembling, he gets it to his mouth and gets it down him. He then pours the last drop from the bottle and drinks it and quivers. "Jesus! I needed that James, so did I. Now lets get the show on the road. There's cattle to be sold."

Silver lifts his ash plant from behind the office door and walks out into the markets like a conductor about to work an orchestra instead of a cattle drover about to steer cattle into the sales ring. James calls for quiet in the auction room as he calls out the terms and conditions of the day's sale. Some wide boy calls out for him to get on with it and a big farmer shouts, "Where's big McCausland? We want paid!"

Silver makes a beeline for the farmer and calls him out of the auction room.

"What's going on Sam?"

"I'll tell you what's going on. We never got paid for last month's cattle and it will mean some farmers won't come back here. All the cheques that Big Billy paid us bounced."

"So what are you going to do about it Sam?"

"We've already made our move."

"What do you mean?"

"I'll tell you what I mean. We have his son and we're keeping him until the big man pays up."

"And if he doesn't pay up, what happens then?"

"What do you think; the boy might have a very bad accident."

Silver grabs Sam by the lapels and tells him, "If anything happens young McCausland, I'll take it very personal. I have known that kid since he was born."

"It's all right for you talking. It's not babby dishes we're talking about Silver, its thousands and I'm owed four hundred and twenty quid myself. So you see it's not a joke. This is for real and some of the wee men could go out of trade and lose their farms. So in times like this desperate men do desperate things."

Silver replies, "and sometimes desperate stupid things. And that's what I'm afraid of."

The auctioneer calls over the public address system, "Phone call for Silver in my office." Silver hurries off and looks around and tells Sam, "I will sort it all out. Don't worry. I promise I'll fix it; the good will of these markets depend on it."

Croaky has been standing behind Sam and Silver unnoticed to them. He slinks back into the auction ring. He then busies himself as he goes about whispering to different farmers. Silver is on the phone in the office looking out the window at Croaky getting agitated with the phone call and wondering what Croaky is up too.

"I can't meet you today but if you call to my house about nine o'clock when it's dark we can take a drive and talk in the car. Okay, that's okay but don't have me sitting in all night waiting on you. Be there or I will come looking for you and you wouldn't want that now Billy would you?"

Chapter 4

That night Silver is sitting in the living room with Mary and he is acting very agitated. "Why don't you go on down to the pub to your mates. Your sitting there like you have pins and needles in your arse."

"I'm waiting on someone to call if you'd like to know and no, I won't be going to the pub so put that in your pipe and smoke it."

"I don't smoke and you can keep your corner boy talk for your cronies. By the way, what were you doing down at the markets telling that Croaky fellow all my business?"

"I didn't tell Croaky McNally any of our business but I'll tell you this. One more night of you not coming home, I'm leaving."

"I don't see anyone holding you back."

"You can make all the clever remarks you want but I mean it this time. I went to my mothers yesterday and yes I can go home at any time she said."

"She would say that; she never liked me anyway and I never liked her. So the feeling's mutual."

"You never liked anyone only yourself, Paddy and that includes me. You're so selfish you think the world revolves around Silver and this town of yours."

"Silver's city you mean. Belfast is a city but then you country ones don't know what a city is."

A car horn sounds and Silver looks at the clock – nine o'clock on the minute. Silver grabs his coat from the back of a chair and walks towards the door and stops. "You know I'm only winding you up Mary."

"Maybe so, Paddy but if you don't come home tonight I won't be here in the morning." Silver slams the door behind him and walks out and sees that it's Billy in the car so he gets in.

McCausland speeds off and Silver tells him to slow down that they're not at Dundrod racetrack.

Billy stops at traffic lights and looks at Silver."I'm in trouble and you're the only man who can get me out of it."

"Why me? Why not go to the cops if they have your young John?"

"I wish it was as simple as that. I need twelve grand or the cops will be looking for me, never mind me going looking for them.

"So what's your story then? What are you going to do? "

"In all honesty I don't know. I can rustle up about three grand but after that I'm broke."

"Have you asked any of your business associates?" Silver laughs, "same old story when you're in trouble for money. I bet they were disappearing like rats from a sinking ship."

"Well big Kane lent me five hundred and big Macklin another scrap dealing man, done the same. The others are either not at home or not interested. It's up to you. Take your pick. Lets go and have a drink down in Peters and I will tell you what I want you to do for me. There's a hundred quid in it for you, if you pull it off."

Billy pulls up outside Peters bar and both men walk in. Billy orders two large whiskeys and a bottle of stout.

"I'm not staying long Peter. So that's all I'll be having. So don't serve me another drink even if I order it myself," says Silver.

"Coming up Silver! Sit down and I'll bring it over to you." Silver and Billy sit in a corner and Billy starts to explain what he wants him to do and that he will hopefully have the money gathered up in a day or two and he can make the exchange for his son John.

"His mother thinks he's away camping. If she knew what was happening she'd get the peelers with out a second thought. Drink up, Paddy. Peter give us the same again for the road."

"No, none for me Peter I'm having an early night."

"Have one more then I'll run you home in the car."

"One more and that's it Billy. I'm serious. I'm having a lot of trouble with Mary."

"Women they're all the same but a few pounds will usually solve that problem."

"Well Mary isn't like that; she's a serious piece of work. In fact she's too good for me."

"Ah catch yourself on Paddy! You run this town and you're going to let a woman tell you what to do."

"She's not just any woman, she's my wife and don't you forget it Billy."

The drinks come up and Peter tells them that Bobby McFarlane sent it up; this drink is on him. Silver stands up and shouts down his thanks to Bobby and asks him to come and join them. After a couple of more drinks Silvers plans to go home have long been forgotten and now he wants to go to the Grand Central Hotel for a late night drink.

"You're right Billy. I'm not going home and Mary can do what ever she wants." Billy slaps him on the back.

"Good man Paddy, a man after my own heart". The drink is flowing and it's getting late and the three men get up and walk out and get into the car.

"Are you fit enough to drive Billy?"

"Yes. Sure we're only going around the corner to the Grand Central Hotel. There's no problem."

"Well take it easy. We don't want to finish up in early graves, do we Bobby?"

"What ever you say Silver, what ever you say." The car stops outside the Grand Central Hotel and the three men walk in and are met by the night porter. "Yes sirs, can I help you?"

"Is the bar still open?" asks Billy.

"Yes," replies the porter, "but it's only open for residents."

"Well I want a room for the night. Sign me in."

"What name is it sir?"

"Patrick McKee."

Billy shouts, "Yes, it's Patrick Joseph McKee, also known as Silver." The porter looks at Billy then at Bobby and both nod at the porter.

"I'm only new here Sir but I'm sure they can accommodate you. This way to the bar sirs. You can still have a drink until twelve o'clock and when you book in I will look after your needs, after that."

Silver, Billy and Bobby walk into the bar, which is vibrant with a piano player, a few women, and there in the corner is none other than Roy Rodgers, the Singing Cowboy. As soon as Silver sees Roy he makes his way over to him and puts his hand out and Roy gets up out of his seat and shakes it. Just then Harry Robinson a local bookmaker puts his arm around Silver and asks him what will he have to drink.

"I'm in company, Harry. Well, the whole company can have a drink. I had a great day at the races. I won twelve grand and I'm going to celebrate with my friends and that includes you and our big friend Billy."

Bobby interrupts, "I'm also in the company Harry."

"Well that included you as well."

Harry turns to Roy; "This is Silver McKee, the hardest street fighting man in the world." Silver asks Roy if he can ask him a question – Roy says, "fire away."

"I always loved your films but I'd love to see Trigger more than anything. I just love that palomino; he's a class act." One of Roy's entourage steps in and tells Silver that Trigger is being stabled in Chichester Street in Wallace Torrens stable in the Thompson's blacksmiths yard. He can go and look him over in the morning. He's not going anywhere until about two o'clock when he will be parading down Royal Avenue - right outside the front door of the hotel.

"We're going to try and make it look like the horse is staying in the hotel.

What a howler!" After a bit of small talk with Roy, Silver notices that Harry and Billy have got them selves in a corner and are talking in what looks like a very private conversation. Bobby walks over to Silver and Roy and asks him for an autograph for his son. Roy duly obliges and asks for his son's name.

"Chip – my boy is called Chip."

Roy asks the porter who seems to be slinking about to get him a sheet of paper and off he goes and returns with a pen and sheet of paper. As Roy is signing his autograph he asks what name to put on it.

"Chip. I know it sounds American but he's as Irish as the green shamrock and he loves horses and you Mr. Rodgers." Bobby thanks Roy for the autograph and announces that he is going home a very happy man who just met his favourite actor and got his autograph for his son. "What a night!" he roars as he makes his way out of the hotel. Roy Rodgers calls the porter and asks him can he take him up to his room as he has had a feeling he wouldn't remember where the room was. The porter duly obliges and as Roy leaves, Silver makes his way over to Harry and Billy.

"What have we here?" asks Silver.

"I've just pulled your friend Billy out of trouble by lending him ten grand."

"Jesus, that's great Harry, you're a decent man."

"I know Silver; I'm expecting the money paid back plus twenty percent, in six months." "Twenty percent, that's a bit steep is it not?"

"Beggars can't be choosers Silver. We should all remember that. Now what are you having to drink?" Harry calls the porter who has returned to the lounge and orders a bottle of champagne.

Billy winks at Silver and calls him into a quiet corner.

"Look Silver, he's lending me ten grand and that will be enough for them farmers to let John go. Along with the two grand I have already scraped up, so no matter what Harry says just agree with him and we can get this deal done tomorrow and everyone will be happy." Silver is handed a glass of champagne and drinks it like water and tells the porter to get him a real drink. A bottle of Guinness and a bottle of beer. "That's like phish mares water, that champagne. Give me a real drink any time. That's rotten that stuff." Billy calls Silver and tells him if he stays the night in the hotel he will lift the tab but he wants him ready for about nine o'clock to do the swap over for his son John. Silver agrees and Billy bids him good night then walks over to Harry and they both shake hands.

"I will call here for you at ten in the morning Silver, so go on up to your room and get a good night's sleep." Billy walks over to the reception desk and has a conversation with the manager who hands him a key. He then walks into the lounge. "Here's your key now remember ten o'clock and be ready. I will have the money and you will deliver it and bring John home."

"No problem. I'm going to bed after I finish this bottle and a halfun."

Billy walks over to Harry and shakes his hand and bids him good night and walks out the door. Harry calls Silver over and asks him to sit down and asks can he have a chat with him. Silver sits down and Harry looks around to see that no one is listening and says, "I don't like that big fuck pot McCausland and I'm out to fuck him over."

"So why are you lending him ten grand if you don't like him?"

"I have a method in my madness. He done me a bad turn one time with a good horse I had and if he thinks I've forgot, he's in for a surprise."

"So, what's your plan Harry? I don't really like him but he's the biggest cattle dealer around at the minute and he dictates, in reality, my job and lots of others," says Silver.

"How would you like to work for me? I could do with a man like you to come to the races and be my minder for want of a better word."

"I never liked the term minding anyone Harry."

"Hold on just listen. You can keep your job in the cattle market and when I need you, you can work for me. It will be like a side job."

* * *

Next morning Silver is awakened by a knock at the door and as he climbs out of bed he is confused as to where he is. "Hold on a minute till I put some clothes on!"

Silver pulls on a shirt and a pair of trousers and opens the door and Billy is standing there as large as life and dressed to kill. Silver beckons him in and Billy throws a small attaché case on the bed and starts making a cup of tea.

"Great these hotels. Tea and biscuits in your room. You're living like a king, Silver."

"I'll be living like a hobo if I don't get round and explain to Mary."

"There you go again, the toughest man in Belfast and you're worrying about the wife." Silver shakes his head and asks Billy to pour him a cup of tea and mumbles.

"I suppose you're right. Women! Who do they think they are?"

"Go on my son! That's the attitude. Don't let anyone mess you about – man, woman or beast."

Silver lifts the cup of tea and spills half of it as he tries to get it to his lips.

"That's me finished with the drink. Look at my hands. I can hardly hold that cup of tea." Billy produces a small bottle of whiskey from his inside pocket and pours a drop of it into Silver's tea. "Get that into you and you will be as right as rain." Silver looks at him in disbelief but drinks the tea and within a few minutes he is washing and singing to himself.

"Now listen Paddy. We have to go to Harry's house and he will give us the money and I have to give him the deeds of my house."

"Jesus, I knew there was a catch. Harry wouldn't have loaned you that amount of money unless you had collateral."

"Well its desperation and the banks won't lend it after all them cheques came back. They'd get the peelers for me."

"I suppose business is business. What's that house of yours worth big man?"

"I suppose on a good day twenty grand, sixteen on a bad day. Now whatever you do don't say anything down in Harry's house. Just humour him. He's a mug."

"Yes he's a mug. He's lending you ten grand at twenty percent and you're giving him the deeds of your house."

"He's some mug. We're the mugs, the ones that loose our money in his offices. You don't gamble Paddy do you?"

"An odd time when I might hear something but all the ones that work for me are gambling maniacs. Especially that McNally fellow." Billy opens the attaché case and starts counting the money and Silvers eyes light up.

"I've never seen as much money in one place in all my life."

"Don't be getting any ideas. Wee John's life might depend on this. In fact it does. So no messing about."

After Silver gets ready both men leave the hotel and walk out and get into Billy's car. "Now we can talk. This is the plan. I will give you twelve grand after we leave Harry's house but I have to take a couple of grand back."

"What do you mean, Billy?"

"Well, there will be Harry's ten. My four but then we come to Harry's. I will take back two grand for stock money. You can't buy cattle without money, Paddy. I need to keep buying and selling. You will bring the money to the Alverno Hotel but don't worry. I will drive you up. I will wait down the road in the wee lay-by after I leave you off. You give the money to whoever it is; he will know you. Get wee John and walk down the road. I will be waiting on you both in the lay-by. It's as simple as that; no messing, and you get a hundred quid."

"I want a deuce or I'm not doing it and I want it up front."

"For God's sake Paddy, I thought we were friends."

"What did you say earlier? Business is business?" Both laugh.

"I will give you it as soon as I come out of Harry's. Ok. Let's go. We're running late. And you know what he's like for time. Harry doesn't hang about."

"How long will it take us to get to his house?"

"About fifteen minutes. He lives on the Larne line."

On arrival at Harry's, wee Tom, his right hand man meets them. "What's the score? Is the boss expecting you?"

"We have an appointment. So move out of the way and let us in."

Tom is a gentle type and he moves out of the way without any persuasion. The three men walk into the large hall and Harry greets them. "What have we here? What's going on?"

"Well, we done a bit of business last night and I'm here to conclude it. Don't you remember?"

"I was drunk last night. So don't believe anything I say when I'm drunk. Come on in anyway and have a cup of tea. You can remind me of the business we discussed. Were you there last night Paddy?"

"I was there and your man Roy Rodgers was there as well."

"Oh..." mutters Tom in his polite voice ... "the place was full of cowboys then." Harry looks at Tom and gives a half laugh. "What about you Paddy? I've seen you in better company. I'm only joking Billy don't take offence. Run that bit of business by me again."

As Billy and Harry discuss the deal, Billy pulls the deeds of his house out of his pocket and sets them on the table. "These deeds, plus fifteen percent in six months time." Harry gets up and laughs; "I think it was twenty percent." "Your right Harry," says Silver. Billy gives Silver a dirty look.

"Ten grand's a lot of money and I'm taking a big chance, but I always fancied that big house of yours on the Malone Road, so I'm willing to take a chance." Both men shake hands and Harry goes to his bookie bag, pulls a large bundle of money and counts out eight bundles.

"Only eight there as far as I can see Harry." Harry scratches his head.

"Is there any more money about the house Tom?" Tom ponders and Harry gives him a sly look.

"There's that two grand you won off Mike, what's his name. You told me to put it in the safe."

"Yes, it's up the stairs. Here be a good man and run up and get it." Harry throws the key to Tom who trots off up the stairs and within minutes arrives down with the money and hands it to Harry. "There you are ten grand. Here,

Tom run up and put those deeds in the safe. I have to admit, Billy, if you default, six months from today I'm taking your house."

"Yes Harry, business is business," says Silver.

"You're one hundred percent Paddy, right on the money, pardon the pun.

Billy starts packing the money neatly into the case and shakes hands with Harry. Silver and Harry walk out the door.

"Where's the exchange-taking place?" asks Harry.

"The Alverno Hotel," replies Silver.

Silver and Billy are no sooner out the door when Harry puts his finger over his mouth to Tom. Both listen until the car drives off and then burst into laughter..."I've waited a long time for this. I'm too old of a cat to be bucked by a kitten. Who does Billy McCausland think he is? I run this town?" Both men laugh uncontrollably.

Billy drives down the road and pulls in to the side and stops the car. He reaches over to the bag, which is clamped between Silvers legs, takes it and counts out two grand and puts it in his pocket. Then starts the car and drives off at speed down the road. He turns to Silver and says, "You shouldn't have told that old fucker where we were going. I never trusted him. He's a two-timer; always looking after himself."

Billy stops the car outside the Alverno and tells Silver not to do anything fancy.

"Do you trust anyone Billy? I don't think you trust yourself. You probably sleep with one eye opened."

"Just you do the job and never mind all the talk. You got your deuce. Now go and earn it."

Billy's demeanour has changed and as Silver gets out of the car he drives off down the road at speed. Silver walks into the hotel and the first person he sees is big Sam and Croaky sitting in the corner.

"It's not you I've to meet Sam is it? And what are you doing here Croaky? Who's looking after the men?"

"Yes, Paddy, I'm the man you have to see. Have you got the money?"

"Have you the boy?"

"Yes. He's up stairs in a room and there's ten men with him; so no messing about." Croaky gets up and walks out as Silver and Sam discuss what way to handle the situation.

About five minute's later the cops burst in and tell everyone to stay where they are. "Where is the boy?" asks one cop.

"He's in a room up the stairs as far as I know," says Silver as the cops run towards the stairs.

"What's that you have mister McKee?"

"It's my clothes. I was staying away from home last night."

"You're going to be staying away from home for a long time. You've got yourself mixed up in something more than you can chew. Can we have a look inside the case please?"

"I told you it's my clothes."

"Well then, you won't mind showing us your clothes."

Silver tries to get out of his chair as young John walks into the room surrounded by cops. He runs over to Silver and throws his arms around his neck.

"I knew you'd save me Silver! I knew it." John starts to cry. Silver gets up again and tries to leave with John but leaves the case on the chair.

"Are you not taking your clothes with you sir?" Silver grabs the case and two police officers grabble with him and as they are pulling and hauling at each other the case bursts open and the money falls out.

"Very expensive clothes you wear McKee. Made out of pound notes..." the cops laugh. "You'll have to come with me Mister McKee. I'm arresting you for being involved in criminal activity."

"What activity would that be?"

"I don't know yet but don't worry we will find something. You're going to jail. You two officers take the boy home to his mother. His father won't be there. I presume he's probably not too far away as usual from all this. When there's a criminal act going on he is usually in the background somewhere. You'll have to come along as well Sam but for the life of me I don't know how you got mixed up with this crowd. You're a decent sort of man. All your confederates fled across the fields when they saw us coming. Pity you didn't do the same Sam but then you don't have anything incriminating on you. But we'll work it all out in the station, let's go." "Why can't Silver go home mister?" asks John.

"I'll tell you why son. We are fed up to back teeth with your hero Silver. He thinks he runs this town but I've news for him, he doesn't. Lets go." The cop takes the case from Silver and tells him and Sam to follow him.

"What about John?" asks Silver.

"He's on his way down to his mother where he should be."

As Silver is getting into the cop car he spies McNally talking to what looks like a plainclothes policeman. Silver scratches his head and climbs into the back seat of the car. Sam gets into the other police car and both cars drive off.

Harry is pacing up and down his living room waving the deeds of Billy's house telling Tom that he has big McCausland by the short and curlies. Tom interjects and tells him there's a police car in the drive and they're coming in. Harry goes to the door and greets the cops and invites them in. The cop walks across the living room and sets the attaché case on the table and asks Harry how much he loaned Billy McCausland.

"I lent him some money to pull him out of a bit of trouble," Harry replies.

"What sort of business was that?"

"Well I did some business with him. That I wouldn't call a loan, in the common sense, but more of a favour."

"Can I ask how much you loaned him and I'd just like to remind you that this is a police investigation and it involves a young man being held to ransom?"

"Look officer, Billy McCausland came here in dire straights and asked me to pull him out of a jam and when he told me the story. I was willing to lend him the money."

"Can I ask how much you loaned him, Mister Robinson?"

"Well I don't think that would be nice, to tell you how much I lent a friend, but if you must know it was ten thousand pounds. Isn't that right Tom?"

"Of course Harry. I helped you to count it out. In fact the serial numbers are in the safe where you told me to put them."

"Have you the serial numbers Mister Robinson? Was there anything untoward about the money or where it came from that made you write the serial numbers down?"

"To be honest I won a large amount of it yesterday at Down Royal races and I just asked Tom to check it over as I was going to ring my bank just in case it was from a robbery. I won it from one man whom I since learned was Big Noel. He's a millionaire, so it was all right. But as you know you can't be too careful in this business. There's a lot of shady people involved in it." The cop sniggers. "Did I say something funny sergeant? No. I was just wondering who this big Noel is and what business he's in to afford losing that kind of money? A few people I rang said he was a sound man but a big loser. That's the game of horse racing. To some big players its only pocket money, ten or twenty grand. To me its a lot of money. So you know we just keep an eye on things and that's why we checked the serial numbers. In any case I may have been robbed. Tom could you get me that sheet with the serial numbers on it and show it to the officer. Is there anything wrong officer? You know I sort of knew what Billy was involved in, something to do with, what was it Tom?" "Oh! He said something about a ransom. In a way it was to safeguard the firm's money and that's probably the real reason we took the serial numbers. It's called backing your self, back in the game. It's like taking out insurance. I told Mister Robinson it was a bad idea to loan Billy such a large amount of money as he sails too close to the wind."

"How much did you say you loaned him again?

"Ten grand isn't that right Tom?"

"Yes, that's right and here's the serial numbers of all the large notes. I think there was about two hundred in fivers or so. We didn't bother taking them, but all the big notes are written down here."

"Can I have a look at that please?"

" Certainly," replies Tom. "It took a wee while but you can never be too careful. There's some unscrupulous people running around. Can I get you some tea officer or something a bit stronger?"

"No thanks, but you are positive you lent him ten grand?"

"Why? Is there a discrepancy or did Billy say something else?

"No we haven't picked him up yet but Silver's down in the barracks and he says it was twelve grand you lent him."

"Well if I loaned him twelve grand, I'd want twelve back. So why should I say another amount? Tom was here and helped me count it out. Sure that Silver fellow is punchy; he doesn't know what day it is."

"That may be the truth but it's his word against yours."

"So whom do you want to believe? A drunk or Tom and I?"

"I never thought of that. So it's your word against his."

"By the way, when can I have my money back sir?"

"You can have it back after the court case as it is now evidence and I think after the court case you won't have a problem."

"That's great Sergeant or what is your rank sir?"

"I am a sergeant. You're right."

"Think of all the interest I will be loosing while I'm waiting on the court case."

"You can get a court order to have the money released to you but I'm looking around this house I don't think its going to break you. Do you and your manager want to make a statement now or come down to the station at your leisure? You see there's a slight problem with the money."

"And what is that? I can't divulge at the moment but you will be informed in time."

"I think we will call down to the station with my solicitor – keep everything on the up and up. By the way, why are you looking for Billy McCausland? Has he done something wrong?"

"No, but Silver says the money belongs to him and he borrowed twelve grand from you. So we need to hear his side of the story. To be honest all we want to know is what McKee was doing with all that money that you say you loaned to Mister McCausland and how it came to be in his hands. Something about going to buy a heard of cattle was the story they told us. Some farmer was going out of trade and was selling out to the big man and then he mentioned his son was in a bit of trouble. Well there's his story, your story and Silver's story, and then there's the truth. I wonder what the truth is?"

"I hope your not implying that I am telling you lies or involved in something illegal sergeant?"

"No, Mister Robinson. I don't think you have done anything wrong but I think McCausland was paying some people off and that's his business but there's just another wee matter we need sorted out."

"And what would that be officer, if you don't mind me asking?"

"You'll find out sooner or later. I'm not divulging that to anyone today and I think McKee is the fall guy in all of this. I never liked him anyway. So if he gets the blame, so be it. On his head be it. He's a big lad McKee and I've no sympathy for him."

"Yes he does tend to run around with shady characters but he's not a bad sort. Likes the odd fight but really no harm in him."

"Ask one of my constables. McKee broke his jaw in six places and he only hit him once. So we owe him one so to speak."

"You're probably right. Anyone that does that to one of your men needs to pay for it."

"I'm going to leave now and I will see you both in the station within the next couple of days.

Don't leave it too long. I don't want to be coming back to your home." "Yes that won't be a problem. Let me show you out sergeant."

* * *

A few weeks later a packed Belfast court is quiet as the clerk of the court calls for silence and for everyone to stand. The Judge walks in takes his seat in the court and starts looking through papers and calls the first case.

"McKee versus Regina is first case your honour." Silver is lead into the box flanked by two prison officers, takes a look at the judge, then looks all around the court. Mary is sitting on the front row along with her mother and about eight of his drovers take up seats around the court. There in a back seat is big Billy and Sam. Silver mouths to one of his drivers.

"Where's Croaky?"

A drover gives him a thumbs down and nods his head. The clerk of the court reads out the charges and asks Silver how he would plead. Silver is bewildered and asks what the charges are.

Could the clerk read them out again.

"One. I repeat that you where in possession of counterfeit money in the Alverno Hotel, in the city of Belfast. Two, that you intended using the counterfeit money to buy cattle or livestock with the full knowledge that the said monies where counterfeit. How do you plead?"

"Not guilty your honor." Silver's solicitor jumps up and tells the court that he is representing Mister McKee and that his client has advised him that he denies all the charges. The prosecutor then stands up and tells the court that there is a prima face case to answer and that McKee had the choice to have his case heard at this court or go in front of a jury. Silvers solicitor asks for an adjournment so he can take further instructions from his client. After a bit of debate the judge adjourns the case to the following week.

"My client will be asking for bail your honour. His wife is here. Please stand up Mrs McKee. She is pregnant and it would be a very hard and difficult time for both my client and his wife, as he is the only bread earner in the household."

The judge asks the prosecutor if he had any objections and he replies that it was a complicated case and as McKee has a record for violence there's a fair chance he might try to intimidate crown witnesses. The judge lifts his head and tells the prosecutor that the defendant hasn't been in trouble for five years and there is nothing to suggest to me he is a man of violence.

"Is there anyone here that can give the defendant a character reference?"

"Yes your honour. I will go bail for Patrick and if need be I will give him a job until the court case arises."

"Approach the bench please." The man walks up to the bench and the judge asks him his name.

"I'm Henry Kane, scrap dealer and horse dealer and I will go bail for this man who is a very good friend of mine."

"Bail is set at two hundred pounds. As soon as the bail is posted you can release the prisoner. Next case."

Silver walks down from the dock and goes to the front of the court and signs for his bail. He walks over and hugs Mary and hugs her mother and tries to apologise for the situation he has put everyone in.

Big Henry whispers to Silver, "I'm not giving you a job. You get back over into the Markets and get your men back to their work. I'll see you in a day or two before the case."

Silver calls Lofty and asks why Croaky isn't at the court and Lofty tells him that Croaky has gone his own way and is working for big Sam. "Now I've got it! That fucker Croaky squealed on me. He left the hotel as soon as I arrived and the next thing the cops come flying in. I'm going to kill him, I swear to God in heaven! I will kill him with my bare hands! Come on Mary, I'll take you and your mum over to the ITL café for a big Belfast fry."

"No go you on. I will see you in the house later. I'm going to see my mother gets home."

"Ah thanks for coming. Are you sure you won't come for breakfast. I haven't had a decent bite to eat in weeks."

"Yes I'm sure. I will meet you at home later."

Silver walks out into the court halls, followed by his drovers and some of his other friends and big McCausland walks over to him.

"What happened that day? There's something not right. Harry says he lent me ten grand and you know it was ten so why did you say twelve?"

"I got it wrong. I was counting your money as well as his and I can't change the story now or I'll go to jail."

"Yes, I know but it doesn't add up and why did Croaky leave the hotel as soon as I walked in. He was along with big Sam and now he's working for him. So Croaky went and got the cops or did you Billy,? Or did Harry? I'll tell you one thing I'm going to find out by hook or by crook. Look Billy there's a good chance I'm going to jail and if I do I'm going to hurt someone when I get out and you better send Mary round a few quid while I'm inside."

"Don't worry about that. I will make sure Mary is looked after but if I don't get that ten grand back and Harry takes my house, that's me out of trade."

"Maybe that's what he wanted from the word go. He's a conniving man you know and that wee Tom fellow who works for him, what's his nickname? The sooner I get to the bottom of this the better and he's the weakest link and that's where I'm going to start."

"I've got news for you. Tom is away to manage a hotel in the Isle of Man, so he won't be easily available."

"Well then. I'm going to see Harry and I will wring his skinny wee neck if he doesn't come clean. Have you his phone number? Can you give me it?" Billy searches his pockets and pulls out a little notebook and Silver pulls it out of his hands and tears the page out of it. "The fun's over Billy.

It's now business and I'm not going to jail on my own and you can take that to your bank."

Silver is drinking in the Black Bull and Croaky walks in. The pub goes quiet. Silver walks over to him and shakes his hand.

"Come on. Have a drink. I'm a free man for a week or two. What do you want to drink?"

"I'll take a bottle of stout." Lofty moves to the back of Croaky and some of the other drovers follow suit and Croaky is now surrounded by his ex-fellow workers. Croaky throws is arms aloft and shouts, "Is this a lynch mob?"

Silver moves the surrounding men away except Lofty and he asks Croaky straight up,

"What's going on?"

"What do you mean?" asks Croaky.

"You're working for big Sam and you were with me for fifteen years. So what happened that day in the hotel?"

"Big Sam asked me to sit with him and as soon as you arrived I was to leave. He doesn't like Belfast but he felt okay when you walked in. So my job was done."

"Tell me then, who phoned the cops or did they just happen to be walking by?"

"Look, if I wanted to phone the cops, as you say, what benefit would it do me and after a life time what makes you think I'm a squealer? Here, fuck you and your bottle of stout! You've just crossed the line, Paddy! I never thought you were like that."

Silver grabs Croaky by the lapels and looks him straight in the eyes and asks, "Are you telling me the truth?"

"I don't think I have to prove myself to you or anyone else in this pub. I'm a Market man and we don't open our mouths as you rightly know."

Silver then settles down. "I'm sorry. Here take a drink. I'm just confused. I don't know who put me in trouble but when I do they're going to pay big time and not in Mickey Mouse money either." Croaky tries to turn away but Silver puts his arm around him. "Will you come back and work for me. I need you. Big Lofty is a great lad but I need someone who won't take any nonsense."

"I'll think about it but I'm going to say this..." Croaky raises his voice... "any man that thinks I'm a squealer, say it now or keep your mouths shut. I'm Croaky McNally and I don't talk." A cheer goes up among the men and Silver orders a drink for all of those in the bar. After about an hour of back slapping and heavy drinking Silver looks at the clock and realises he has to go home.

Mary would be waiting.

"I'm away on home lads. See you all bright and early in the morning and that includes you Croaky."

* * *

Next morning Silver is walking about the Markets and his mind is somewhere else. He can't work out who owned the counterfeit money but he has it in his head that it was Harry and nothings going to change that. Suddenly a big Mercedes pulls into the market yard and Harry gets out and walks over to Silver.

"Look, Paddy, I've been good to you over the years, so what's all this business about me lending big McCausland twelve grand when you know it was ten?

"I was counting Billy's money as well and I got mixed up. What I want to know is who owned the counterfeit money and who called the cops?"

"Well you saw my money in my house and we counted it out in front of you. How in heavens name did you get so mixed up?"

"Okay. I agree with you. But who owned the counterfeit money? Billy's not going to do something like that when his own son's life is at stake. What do you think?"

"I think Billy's money was the counterfeit."

"No I disagree. He wouldn't do that and maybe get his son killed, now would he? Look, let me tell you Paddy, there's two worlds: one is the honest guys world, the one that goes to work every day; then there's the business world where money takes over and talks all languages."

"By the way, what about that wee guy Tom who worked for you? Where's he now?"

"He's like a whole lot more. He was beginning to think he owned the business and that doesn't work with me. Come down to my office tomorrow, I want to talk to you in private. Make it about eleven o'clock." Harry gets into his car and drives off.

* * *

Some time later Silver is standing in a ward of the Royal Victoria hospital maternity ward as Mary nurses their newborn daughter, Anne. "Do you want to hold her Paddy?" asks Mary.

"No, not at the minute..." Silver looks at his big broad hands and then at the baby, "no way could I hold that wee thing".

"This wee thing is our daughter. Not a foal or a calf and don't forget it. And her name is Anne whether you like it or not. You can pick her second name after your mother but I'm choosing her first name."

"Okay, I've no problem with that. Mary you know what I mean that court case is coming up in a fortnight and theres a good chance I will go to jail, so we better get her christened soon."

"I suppose you wanted a wee lad so he could follow in your footsteps in the market, driving cows and sheep in to them pens. Well this girl is going to get educated and have a good job and maybe just maybe become a teacher or some thing good in life."

"Let me have another look at her Mary?" Silver moves closer to the bed and looks at the baby and remarks that's she has lovely blue eyes, just like her dad and blonde hair to boot. "Sure she has my Ma's nose. She's a real wee McKee."

"If you want to know, I think she will be a red head like her mother and I only hope if she gets married she finds a better husband than I did." A nurse walks into the hospital ward ringing a large bell. This is to inform everyone that visiting is over and Silver leans over and kisses Mary on the cheek.

"I'll go away on here, and I will be up to see you tomorrow at two o'clock. Isn't that visiting time?

"Don't bother your barney. Order a taxi and be ready at ten o'clock in the morning. I'm getting out and I hope that house of ours is clean and tidy."

"What are you saying woman? You're only in. You need some rest."

"I know I need rest but the hospital needs the bed. They're sending me home so you be here at ten sharp and don't be late."

"Jesus! I will have to go and get a car organised for the morning."

"Just get a taxi. Never mind your big shot friends and borrowing their cars. Just be here in a taxi at ten. If you're late don't bother coming because I'll be away on home, the child and me."

"Okay woman don't be shouting! I'll be here at ten sharp. By the way she's beautiful, just like her mother."

"Just like my arse! Get you on your way and none of that oul soft talk. Keep that for your cronies." Silver tip toes off down the ward, so as not to be making too much noise with his clickedy clack steel tipped boots but as soon as he gets out of the ward his shoulders are swinging and his heels are clickedy clacking and he smiles and mutters to himself, "I'm a father. I'm a father. It's time to wise up."

Silver walks out of the hospital grounds and the first thing he sees is the Oak Bar and decides to go in for a drink. As Silver walks into the public bar he sees an old friend of his – Dan Fenton. Silver and Dan shake hands and Dan orders him a drink.

"What has you up this way, Paddy?" asks Dan.

"Mary is over in the maternity. She just had a baby and I came in for one. My heads bursting. Never liked the inside of hospitals."

Dan shouts out around the bar, "Did youse hear that Silver's wife had their first child. Now we can all wet its head. Give them all a halfun and give Paddy a glass of Bushmills. This is a very special occasion." Silver whispers in Dan's ear that he doesn't want any commotion or fuss that he only came in for one. "Get that glass of Bush into you. It's not every day you become a father." Silver drinks the bush whiskey and says to Dan that he has to go but Dan persuades him to stay for another one drink.

That night Dan and Silver are walking down the Falls Road singing and dancing as they make their way to Dan's house. As soon as they walk in Dan tells his wife Lizzie that they were celebrating Silver becoming a dad and could she make up the back room for him as he couldn't go home in a drunken state to an empty house in the market.

"Your dinner is in the oven and I'm sure its burnt to a cinder. I'll make Paddy a fry."

"No, no, no, Missus, just get me a bed! I've to be over at the hospital at ten in the morning sharp. She's getting out tomorrow." Dan tells Lizzie to share his dinner on two plates and Silver can half. Lizzie duly obliges and Dan and Silver get stuck in to their plate of cabbage and ribs. After about a half an hour Dan leads Silver up to the back room and shows him in and Silver falls flat on his back on the bed and falls fast asleep.

Next morning Dan is up early and Silver is fast still asleep in the backroom. He tells Lizzie to let him sleep it off. Just as Dan is having his breakfast he hears Silver getting up and he tells Lizzie to make Silver a fry. Lizzie looks at the clock and sees it is half nine and remembers what Silver had told them that he had to be at the hospital for ten o'clock sharp.

"Run you down the street Dan and get your big man Sherry the taxi man. If you can't get him get somebody else up here quick or Mary will never speak to us again." Dan pulls on his shoes and runs out the door and arrives out of breath at the taxi mans house and raps the door. A big man comes to the door and asks what he wants.

"I need a taxi as soon as possible. "

"I'm not working today. It's my day off, but I can phone you one out of Silver Cabs." Dan tells him that the person needs to be at the Royal for ten sharp and they don't have time. "I will phone the depot and there'll be a taxi up in half an hour."

"Look, that would be too late" says Dan. "Well it's the best I can do. The wife and me are going to Larne today to visit her mother. We always go there on my day off."

"Look, there's two pounds in it for you."

"It doesn't matter if there's fifty pound in it. You know what women are like?"

"Would it make any difference if I said it was for Silver McKee?"

"Now that would make some difference all right. That man saved my bacon one night after a crowd got round me in the Market district and it was getting into a nasty situation and Silver stepped in. So where is he? I'm your man."

"He's in my house in 12 Balkan Street; we will be standing at the front door. No worries. I will be there in two minutes. In fact you come with me. Wait 'til I get my coat. Anything for to be able to do a turn for Silver McKee."

Silver has had a shave and tidied himself up and as he gets into the taxi he shouts to Dan and Lizzie that they will be invited to the christening and won't be taking no for an answer. Both Lizzie and Dan agree and the taxi drives off. Silver asks the driver what the time is. He is told it is now twenty past ten.

"I need to be at the maternity in ten minutes."

"Don't worry. I will get you there in time. It's not far. Do you remember the night you stopped a crowd in the markets who where giving me a hard time. You stepped in and I got away."

"I'll never forget it so this fare is on me. Where are we going after the Royal?"

"Down to the market to my house and I haven't even cleaned it up for the wife and the new baby."

"Ach! You'll be alright. Your wife will understand you were out wetting the baby's head. There wont be a problem."

"Son, don't mention where you picked me up, just let me do the talking. She will be none the wiser."

"What ever you say. You're the boss." The driver has a big smile on his face as he pulls up at the maternity right on half past ten. Silver jumps out and trots up the corridor only to be met by Mary carrying Anne, making their way towards the door. "Can you never be on time Paddy? You think the world revolves around you. For God sake catch yourself on; another man would have been here from nine o'clock. But you're last minute Arthur. You'll be late for your own funeral."

"Well I hope that won't be for a while. Come on! I've a cab waiting outside." Silver takes the baby Anne from Mary as she climbs into the back seat. Then he hands her back the baby and tries to get in beside her.

"Get you into the front; the smell of the drink of your breath will make the child sick.Take us home driver and no stops on the way son. Directly to 9 Market Street and I hope you have the house clean and tidy and the fire lit. A newborn baby needs plenty of heat you know. Silver gets in the front and looks at the driver sternly. He tries to explain that he hadn't time to light the fire, as he had to go to work before he came up to the hospital.

"That's right Missus," says the driver, "I lifted him up the Falls. He was doing some kind of business, isn't that right Silver?" Silver looks at the taxi driver again but in amazement this time telling Mary that he was up seeing Henry Kane about the court case. Just in case he needs his bail renewed.

"Well the last I heard Big Henry doesn't drink anymore. So I think you may have been out all night by the sounds of things." The taxi pulls up outside Silver's house and he jumps out and opens the hall door and walks back and takes the baby off Mary. She then gets out and takes the baby and walks into the house. Silver goes to pay the driver and he says that the fare was on him and bids Silver good luck with the new baby.

"I wish you hadn't mentioned the Falls Road but anyway thanks son. Hopefully see you around, when I need another taxi."

"You'll have to pay for the next one". Both laugh as Silver closes the door and the taxi drives off. Silver walks into the house and Mary is kneeling down trying to light the fire. Anne is in a baby manger that Mary bought some time earlier. Anne is crying loudly and Silver is holding his head.

"I told you to light the fire for the baby coming home. She will get a pleurisy or TB if she's not lucky." Silver lifts Mary from the front of the fire and starts about trying to light it but he realises that God may have given him hands for hard work and fighting but he's useless at ordinary household chores. After a few minutes the fire is blazing up the chimney and Mary has the baby on her knee and is breast-feeding it.

"Jesus woman put that away. If anyone walks in they'll think I've gone mad."

"Now why would they think you've gone mad. It isn't your breast. Now put me on a cup of tea. At least you can do that or is it too much to ask." Silver walks to the hall and slams the door tight and walks into the living room.

"There'll be no one coming into my house while you doing that. Could you not give her a bottle like everyone else?"

"This is natural; theres enough sucking on bottles in this house. You smell like a brewery. Now go and clean your teeth. I'm just wondering where you slept last night. All I hope, no not hope ... you better not have slept with anyone else."

"Woman dear. You're looking at the wrong man. I would never go out with another woman.

Honest to God. May he strike me dead if I tell a lie?"

Mary waits for a moment. "God must be on his lunch hour. You're a lying bastard and you should be dead long time ago." Silver laughs it off and goes back into the scullery and continues making the tea.

* * *

A week or so later St Malachy's chapel is packed as Anne, the baby, is being christened. Sally Rogers and big Lofty are godparents and all the people from the market area are there looking on. After the christening is finished Silver and Mary along with Sally Rogers and lofty are standing on the steps as some photographs are taken, and everyone is trying to shake Silver's hand.

"All round to the Black Bull in an hour. The drinks are on me. Everyone is welcome."

Out of the crowd steps big McCausland and pulls Silver aside. "I've a month or so to pay Harry and if I don't I'm going to lose my house." Silver tells Billy that this is neither the time nor the place and if he doesn't get out of the way he'll be feeling the weight of one of his fists.

"Come around to the Black Bull. We can talk about it then but never in your life talk about that business in front of my family and friends." Billy slinks back into the crowd and Croaky pulls Silver's coat and whispers into his ear that Harry Robinson is around in the pub slobbering about someone has stolen his money and if he doesn't get his full ten grand back he's keeping Billy's house. Silver scans the crowd and walks over to Billy and apologises and tells him he will talk to Harry and get something ironed out. Both shake hands and arrange to have a yarn in the pub.

About an hour later Silver walks into the pub and is met by loud cheering. Everyone wants to shake his hand. Croaky orders him a large Bushmills and a bottle of stout and tells Silver that the pub has put a few sandwiches on and a pot of soup.

"I could do with a bowl of soup before I get that drink into me. My stomach is on the bum." Billy is sitting over in a corner like a lost man and Silver walks over and sits down. "Look, Paddy, you delivered the money and you know that bastard Harry was the only one that could have had the phoney money. Isn't that right? It was never out of yours or my sight and you know that."

"Well, we did stop at your house and you brought the case in with you so as you could put your stake in the case."

"I know, but do you think I'm going to endanger my own son John's life for a couple of grand?"

"Now let me speak. I am probably going to jail and if I find out who done the stroke I'm going to hurt him or them badly. I'm going nap on that wee Tom. He has disappeared sharpish and he was always a move maker."

"Look Silver anything Tom done or didn't do it was at Harry's behest. He wouldn't fuck you or me. He'd be to afraid but if you look at it Harry's going to get my house and that will be me out of trade."

"Again! You've been in and out of trade all your life big man, you'll bounce back just like always. Leave it with me. I will talk to Harry when he comes in. He's around in Lynches' getting drunk before he comes around here slobbering. I can read him like a book. You go on home and let me deal with it and I promise you I will look after your interests the best I can. Both men shake hands and Billy walks out the front door as Silver shouts, "I'll talk to you at the court next week."

A few minutes later a singsong is in progress and in walks Harry with some would-be hard man and heads straight for Silver. He starts shouting the odds at Silver, telling him what he's going to do if he doesn't get his money back. Silver asks him is he implying that he took it and Harry replies that he doesn't care who took it as long as he gets it back. Silver interrupts him and tells him that he was slabbering round in Lynch's Bar, that he was going to take Billy's house lock stock and barrel. "That's rich, a slabber slabbering about a slabber, slabbering,"

Silver grips him by the throat and tells him, "You're lucky I'm celebrating my daughter's christening today or I'd break your skinny neck." Just at that Harry's minder steps forward and informs Silver that he won't be breaking anyone's neck, especially anyone that's with him and he'd better back off. Silver asks Harry who his new minder is and Harry says that he's an ex-boxer. The minder steps forward and informs Silver he can speak for himself and that he's a McIlvenny and he will stand by Harry if there's any trouble. Silver lashes out and connects on McIlvenny's jaw and he falls like a sack of potatoes.

"You've got it all wrong Silver. Sure I told you I had a job for you after the court case. He's just a hanger on."

"I'd advise you and the big lad,"who is just coming around, "to get going before I really start." Silver pulls off his coat and rolls up his sleeves as Harry helps McIlvenny out the door. "Remember this Robinson. I'm shooting for big McCausland, don't be messing him about and he'd better get his house back you thieving wee runt of a man."

As Harry and McIlvenny are going out the door Silver's friends start singing, "Go home you bum, go home."

Chapter 5

A few weeks later Silver is standing smartly dressed in the dock of the Belfast courts with two cops flanking him. The judge lifts his head and looks at Silver. "I think you, McKee, have been used but you allowed that to happen and you are responsible for your actions. For those that are behind this scheme and not in front of this court and should be, I'm going to take that all into account. The fact that you didn't try to buy anything with the counterfeit money, is in my mind proof that you were used. Having said that I'm going to take a lenient view on this case. I sentence you to three years in prison for being in possession of the counterfeit money..." The court goes silent and Mary is given a glass of water,"... and three months for common assault on the police officer that arrested you..." There is uproar in the court. "... Further more, I'm going to suspend the three years in prison for three years but I'm going to enforce the three months for assault. Take him down."

Silver looks down at Mary and then looks at his solicitor who shrugs his shoulders and he's lead away by the two cops. That afternoon Silver arrives at Crumlin road jail and like all new prisoners he is brought in front of the governor.

"Who have we here? Patrick Joseph McKee. Ah, your name precedes you. I've heard a lot of talk about you. I'm from Belfast myself and I've heard on the grapevine that this isn't your modus operandi and you were used. All I can say is keep your head down and you will be out in six weeks time. Keep your nose clean and you'll not even notice the time going by. Where would you like to work – inside or outside McKee?"

"I'd like outside sir. I'm used to the outdoors."

"Ok put him in the wood yard and bring the next prisoner in."

"Thanks sir", says Silver. He is lead away and brought to be issued with his prison uniform and is then accompanied to his cell where he meets a wee small fellow whom he knows from the Shankill Road.

"Sandy McCoy! What are you doing in here?"

"Six months, for stealing a bit of scrap lead. Big Davy is down the wing. We got done together but they wouldn't let us share a cell. Thank God big Davy couldn't do an hour, he would do my head in. We thought it was scrap and found out later it was ships' ballast. What a laugh!"

"By the way Sandy, I can't do an hour but I have to get on with it and I'm taking the easier, softer option; head down, keeping out of trouble."

Next morning Silver and Sandy are sitting in the canteen eating their watery porridge when big Davy, a larger than life fellow, walks up to both of them and looks at Silver. "What are you doing in here Paddy?"

"Time. Like everyone else, Davy. But it's not a holiday camp. Now sit down and don't be making a fuss."

"Never thought I'd see the day that Silver McKee would be in jail. What you in for?"

"I was caught with counterfeit money and I only wish I knew where it came from because it wasn't mine."

"Now that's interesting. I know there was a lot of phoney money came up from Dublin. A gangster called big Noel – a real shrewdy, tried to sell me some of it for five bob in the pound. I bid him two bob. That's what its worth but he wouldn't have a deal."

"Big Noel..." ponders Silver. "Where have I heard that name before? I'm sure he was mentioned in dispatches somewhere along the way. He's a big player isn't he Sandy?"

"He's a big free state bastard. You couldn't trust him if you reared him." Nothing has changed with Sandy, he still hates the world. The three men all laugh and get on with eating their breakfast.

After a day in the woodyard, being asked a million questions by all the cons, Silver says to himself, "I wish I had taken a job inside in the kitchen or somewhere else. They all want to know your life story out here." That night as he is lying in his bunk and Sandy is in the top bunk singing away, Silver asks him, "Sandy, are you married or single."

"No chance of me getting married. Are you mad? I'm going to enjoy myself when I get out of here."

"Doing what, stealing scrap lead?" Both laugh. After a few weeks in the woodyard Silver is brought before the governor.

"I have brought you up here to tell you that you are being transferred into the kitchen. My officers tell me that since you started in the woodyard no one is doing any work. They are all standing listening to your stories and that's not good for morale. Before you say it, I know it's not your fault but I have to do something to rectify the situation." The governor tells the two prison officers to wait outside as he wants to talk to McKee in private. "Did you really knock a bull out with one punch Silver, or is it just another one of the usual Belfast tales of exaggeration?"

"To be honest sir, does it really matter what I did or didn't do. All I know is I'm in here trying to keep my head down and not get into any trouble and get out of here."

"Yes. I agree with you. I just heard the story a few years ago and wondered was any man capable of that. Well I understand, so it will be the kitchen for the rest of your time and try not to be telling stories, as we need the food to be on time?" Both men laugh. The governor calls the guards in and they come in to escort Silver out. Just as Silver is going out the door he turns and says to the governor, "you know that story you asked me about, its true every word of it."

After finishing his time working in the kitchen it is Silver's last night in Crumlin road jail. As he is lying on his bunk he shouts up to Sandy on the top bunk. "It wasn't that bad in here. Three meals a day and plenty of chocolate. What else would a man want?"

"I know what I'd want – to be home eating my Ma's food. The grub in here is stinking. Big Davy has lost two stone already. If it keeps going on he'll be like a wafer when he gets out."

"Yes, Sandy but I worked in the kitchen." Both men break into a fit of laughing. The next morning Silver shakes hands with Sandy and as he's putting on his civilian clothes, he hands Sandy all his tobacco and tells him he will see him and Davy when they get out. "I want to know more about the big Dublin man."

"Big Noel?" asks Sandy.

"Yes that's him."

Silver walks down the wing and out the front gate and the first person he sees is Mary with the baby in a pram. Silver kisses her and lifts Anne out of the pram and hugs her. "You didn't push that pram the whole way up here did you?"

"Well it didn't push its self up. Of course I pushed it up and I'll push it back down."

"No way. I've a couple of quid here. We're getting a taxi home." Silver walks to the front of the Crumlin Road and within a few minutes he waves down a taxi and he loads the pram into the boot. Mary, Anne, and Silver get in.

"Jesus it's Silver McKee. The last time I saw you, Stormy was knocking the rump out of you up and down the Shankill."

"Just drive the car son or I'll thump you up and down this road."

"Well Stormy is saying it to everyone in the Rex Bar and bumming and blowing about it."

"You tell Stormy, the two-faced fucker, I'll be back and nobody ever knocked my rump in as you call it – nobody and I mean nobody. The taxi pulls up at Silver's house and he gets the pram out of the boot and is trying to assemble the pram when Mary pushes him out of the way.

"You haven't hands to bless your self. Now get out of the way and hold

Anne." Silver goes to his pocket and is leaning in the window paying the taxi driver.

"Listen son, you've a lot to learn and one thing is know when to speak and when not too and you need to learn when not too." The taxi driver roars off leaving Silver with his money still in his hand. Silver laughs and goes and opens the front door and lets Mary in.

After a few days Silver appears at the market and is gathering his men up when James Allams the owner of the cattle market approaches him and asks can he have a word.

"Surely James. What can I do for you?"

"It's a touchy subject but we're withdrawing your contract. Croaky is now running the men. I'm sorry but that's what happens when you get on the wrong side of the farmers. They've said they don't want you handling their cattle or sheep. So I'd rather you didn't come back here. I know I can't stop you but I'd rather you didn't show your face here any more. I'm sorry." James turns and walks away.

* * *

Silver is sitting having a cup of tea with Mary and she asks him why he's so quiet. "I'll tell you why. I'm out of a job and I don't know anything other than working with cattle. So what am I going to do? An ex-jail bird that no one wants to know or employ."

"Don't worry, something will come along now. Would you run down to English's bakery and get me a batch loaf and a couple of broken buns for a cup of tea." Silver gets up, grabs his coat and fixes his tie and checks he has some change. "Have you enough Paddy?"

"Well I think I have enough for a loaf and some broken buns. Sure some of the boys will be on the desk I'll probably get them buck shee."

"I don't want them for nothing. If I wanted things for nothing I'd start begging in the street and I'm not about to do that. Here's a half a crown, you can also get two soda farls. Get a quarter of cheese in McReynolds shop and we can toast the sodas."

"Mary you know something about you. It's the simple things in life that you enjoy and I love you for that but things are going to get tough."

"Well, we haven't starved a winter yet and I don't think we're about to now."

Silver arrives at the bakery a large sprawling building that is only at the bottom of the street. He is met by men carrying placards reading,

OFFICIAL STRIKE
IRISH GENERAL WORKERS UNION

Silver goes to walk past the picket line and an old friend of his, Shaky McCann steps forward and tells him that the workers are on strike and no one is breaking the picket lines.

"Jesus Shaky, all I'm looking is a loaf and a couple of soda farls. I'm not asking for the moon."

"Silver, do you think you'd have to ask me twice if I could give you what you want. There's not a loaf in the place. Sure the mice are moving out."

"So where would I get a loaf?"

"Silver if you get a loaf in town today it will be a miracle. There's not a loaf of bread to be got. I'm sorry. We're on strike and the ovens haven't even been lit today and if you had of been in a union, James Allams couldn't have sacked you."

"How do you know about that?"

"It's all over the Market. Croaky is running the show and you got sacked."

"For Gods sake I need a loaf of bread. I couldn't eat anything without a slice of bread."

"I know Silver, but I swear to God there's not a bit of bread in my own house and Margaret loves bread so I will have to make her a few pancakes when I go home. If there was a loaf in there you know I'd slip it out to you."

"Fair play to you, Shaky, you were always a sound man and I think I understand what your doing. Can I ask you a question?"

"Yes, Silver what is it?"

"If I had been a union member would James Allams be able to sack me. Give me a straight answer – no bull shit."

"If you were a member of a union Paddy and had your men behind you, there would be no chance of you being sacked. There's a pub in Dublin and it hasn't opened in twelve years over a man being sacked for nothing."

"Twelve months you mean Shaky."

"No, I mean twelve years and that's what's called strength." Silver bids Shaky good luck and heads back to the house empty handed. As he enters the living room Mary asks him where the loaf and soda farls are and he explains that the bakery workers are on strike.

"On strike what for?"

"For more money and better conditions. I heard one of them shouting. Sure the whole Market is fed out of English's bakery. It better not last long or we will all starve. Well we're going to have to like it or lump it. Shaky is going home to make Margaret crumpets or pancakes that's how bad it is and he's a baker in the place. So if he can't get a loaf what chance have I?"

A couple of days later a young fellow knocks the door of Silver's house and he gets up and opens the door. "Silver!" he blurts out, "P.G. McQuaid is looking for you. He's in the Black Bull."

"If you go to that pub don't be coming back. I'm sick and tired of 'he'll meet you in the

Black Bull. I just went in for one...' for God's sake Paddy, give it a break."

"But missus, he only wants Silver to help him sell bread he brought down from the Free State."

"What did you say, sell bread? Well at least you will get a loaf if I run on over there. The least I can do is bring back a loaf."

"I'd love a round of toast," says Mary. Silver gets his coat and as he's walking out he gives Mary a peck on the cheek.

"That's Cheeky Charley. He runs messages for dealers and sells stuff in Castle Street. I may get a few bob along with a couple of loaves." Silver walks out and Charlie and he make their way to the Black Bull. As they enter the door, P.G. jumps up and throws his arms around Silver and tells him he needs a pitch to sell a vanload of bread he has outside. Silver tells him to keep his voice down. "Does he not know that the biggest employer in the Market is English's Bakery and they'd get hung for selling bread around here?"

"I know but where is neutral? I've a thousand loaves in the back of that van outside and if I don't sell them today they'll go stale and I will have done my money!"

Cheeky Charlie buts in. "Yeah, P.G. you'd do your dough." Charlie bursts out laughing and Silver grabs him and tells him to be quiet.

"Where did you dig him up P.G.? He's a nuisance at times."

"Castle Street. He was selling candy apples and I asked him where could I get in touch with you so he brought me here. He then went over to your house and brought you here."

"I suppose he's alright. Just that woman of mine is getting on to me and him roaring and shouting. It's too much for one man." Silver ponders for a minute and says. "I know a good spot in High Street – an old bomb site and it's neutral. And if you get round and set up, Charlie is a good salesman but I don't think that matters. Bread is like gold dust and before we go anywhere I need two loaves."

"Okay, there's a half a dozen in the cab says P.G."

Silver calls the barman and asks for a large carry out bag. The barman duly obliges and Silver, P.G. and Charlie walk out to the van, an old 3-Way Austin. P.G. looks around him and lifts two loaves and puts them in Silver's bag. Silver hands the bag to Charlie. "Bring them two loaves around to my house and tell Mary to give one to my Ma." Charlie takes the bag and asks where to meet them. "We will be in High Street where Tie the Boy breaks his chains on the waste ground. Now let me give you a wee warning young lad. If I come home tonight and there's no bread in my house you may leave the country."

"Don't worry Silver, I'm on my way but..."

"No buts, no maybes, no how's. If there's no loaf in my house when I come back you better be on the Heysham boat." Charlie heads off to deliver the bread and Silver gets into the van with P.G. and they drive to the High Street waste ground and P.G. does what Silver tells him and drives straight up the kerb onto the waste ground and parks. Silver tells him to turn the van so as it's pointed out in case they have to make a quick getaway. They get out of the van and P.G. opens the back doors and drops down the tailgate and jumps up. "Stall a minute till that other bucko comes back. You will need a hand. I will stand here in case there's any trouble." Charlie is running up High Street and his mother Ena stops him.

"Hey Charlie! Just the man I'm looking for. Where would I get a loaf for your da's supper tonight?" Charlie whispers to her to follow him and she may be in luck and they both walk up to the site. Silver calls Charlie and tells him P.G. is going to do the selling. He will hand the bread to you and you will take the money off the customer and not to be fly, as it will all be counted.

"So don't be getting P.G.'s money mixed up with your own."

"I'm not like that Silver. Honest to God. Ask my Ma. There she is."

"Your as straight as the hairpin bend and what am I doing explaining myself to you? Just do as your told." P.G. starts shouting."

"Bread for sale! A shilling a loaf!"

Ena asks, "Can I have two mister?"

"No, missus. It's one a piece for everyone and that includes my own wife."

"Ach, give her two. P.G. That's my Ma, our first customer. Give her the two for luck." P.G. duly obliges and Ena pays Charlie and trots off. Every one Ena meets in a busy Belfast, she stops to tell them that they're selling bread down the street. A large crowd soon gathers and the bread is flying out of the back of the van when Tie the Boy walks over to P.G. Tie the Boy is built like a house and breaks chain that people tie around him, hence the name Tie the Boy. He is stripped to his waist and covered in oil and is telling P.G. to move, as he can't earn anything as the van is blocking his show. He makes a grab for Tie the Boy and Charlie runs over to get Silver who is propping up a wall. Silver walks over and asks what the trouble is. Tie the Boy tells him to mind his own business and Silver says to him. "I'm going to show you something. If you don't go away, I'll wrap them chains around your neck and no one will open them." Silver calls to P.G. "Throw me down a penny." P.G. looks at him, "A penny?" "Yes, a brown penny." P.G. tosses the penny down and Silver catches it and gets it between his fingers and thumb and bends it closed. "Now Tie the Boy or whatever your name is, take yourself off. We will be finished in an hour or so."

Charlie shouts, "What a job Silver!"

"Up or down; what way do you want it?" Silver asks Tie the Boy.

"I didn't know you were with him, Silver," says Tie the Boy as he realises it's Silver McKee.

"Well now you know. So get back to what you do best acting Tarzan." Tie the Boy walks away with his head down and out of the crowd walks Trevor and approaches Silver. Silver sees him and puts his hand out and both men shake hands.

"I'm giving you a warning because I know you're having a bad time and have lost your job but did you ever think of the men on strike and by selling this free state bread you're weakening their position and prolonging the strike."

"Trevor I need a few quid and if I sit in the house I won't earn a bob. So I have to do something."

"Do you know where the most people who work in English's bakery are from?"

"Of course I do. I'm not that stupid. They're from the market. My own district. Sure I'm not that dopey."

Cheeky Charlie shouts "Last dozen loaves! Come and get them there will be no more after these. You can roast it or toast it, have ham, spam, plum or apple jam on it! Last dozen! Up you come!

Two loaves for my wee neighbours Mister and Mrs. Connolly PG and that's the last." Trevor and Silver are talking and Charlie runs over and tells them that they are sold out.

"Tell P.G. to meet me in the Elsinore hotel; we can't go back to the Black Bull. They'll lynch him and maybe me as well if we go back there."

"And they'd be right Paddy; he's an opportunist of the first degree."

"And what's wrong with that Trevor? It's the way of the world; he's a dealing man."

Trevor walks away and shouts back to Silver, "Not my world! There's no place for me in a world like that." P.G. and Charlie drive off and Silver walks up towards Castle Street and cuts through Chapel Lane where he meets an old friend, Skinny Reynolds.

"You not working young Reynolds?"

"No, we're on strike and the boys are gathering up. There's a countryman selling bread down in High Street. The cheek of him in our town and all us market men on strike."

"Do you want me to go down with you?"

"Jesus, that would be great, Silver. We need a bit of support." Silver is laughing to himself as he tells Skinny to lead the way and asks him where he is selling the bread. "Down on the waste ground, in High Street beside Speckman's shop." Silver dallies behind him and as they reach the site they see that it's full of the striking bakery workers. Skinny walks over to them and tells them that Silver is supporting them. A large cheer goes up and Trevor walks out of the crowd and calls Silver aside.

"Pick your side. I won't say nothing but it's one or the other. You can't have it both ways."

"I'm with youse!" cries Silver... "but now I have somewhere to go with Trevor."

"You would be a good figurehead for this crowd but remember, it's one way or the other Paddy, or I will tell the men what you have being doing."

"Look, Trevor I needed a few quid and all I done was stand in the background. It was that wee bastard Cheeky Charlie that brought your man to me."

Trevor looks at him and says, "I believe you, but millions wouldn't." Both men shake and Silver walks off.

Skinny runs after Silver. "Are you with us Paddy?"

Silver replies, "Yes, one hundred percent." Silver walks into the Elsinore hotel and P.G. and Charlie are sitting at a table counting the money. He walks over to P.G. sticks his hand out and P.G. hands him a five-pound note. "Right. I'm away home and Charlie or whatever your name is, if I ever hear you talking about todays dealings I will strangle you."

"You'll never hear me talking out of school. It's not what I do."

"Just remember I had nothing to do with todays shenanigans and that's the way its stays and I mean it. Don't breathe a word. By the way did you leave them loaves in my house?"

"No I left them next door. Your wife wasn't in so I left the bag with Mrs. Gorman next door."

"I may run home. "If she opens that bag, it will be all over the market that Silver has bread and they'll want to know where I got it. Thanks! I have to go and you; if I sent you for a fish supper you'd come back with a lollipop, you stupid fucker." Silver walks out the door and rushes towards home. As he reaches his house he notices the hall door is open so Mary must be back. As he rushes in, he asks her did she get the parcel from next door.

"No I didn't."

"I'll go in and get it. And don't mention bread to anyone." Silver knocks Mrs. Gorman's door and a wee woman answers the door.

"Oh! You must be here for the bag."

"Yes a friend left it for me. I don't even know what's in it."

"It smells like bread to me but everything smells like bread living beside the bakery." The wee woman goes back into the house and comes back and hands Silver the bag. I could have sworn it was bread in that bag."

"Well, Maggie, if it were bread, would you like half a loaf."

"Would I like a half a loaf? I'd kill for a round of bread now after a week without any?"

"I'll be back in a minute." Silver goes into his own house, goes out to the scullery and takes one of the loaves out and cuts it in half. Puts it in the bag and brings it into Mrs. Gorman. As he hands her it he tells her not to say a word. "A friend of mine brought it up from Dublin on the train."

"Mums the word, Silver, and thanks, you're a decent man."

Chapter 6

Silver is sitting over a bottle of stout killing time when the door opens and in walks Jimmy Connolly, a well-known bookmaker from up the Falls Road. "Hello Paddy. How's it going. I heard you're a bread server now," Jimmy sniggers. Silver gets up from his stool and walks towards him and tells him in no uncertain terms to be quiet. "I'm only slagging. Can you not take a joke?"

"Joke? Half the people in the Market aren't talking to me and you're making a corner boy joke about it. It nearly cost me my marriage."

"Jesus, I'm sorry. I didn't think it was that bad. Anyway, what are you having?"

"Nothing. I'm just killing time here. The tank is low so I couldn't buy you a drink back."

"It's not that bad, is it? And anyway did I ask you to buy me one back?" Jimmy orders two bottles of stout and perches himself up at the bar, beside Silver.

"I'm in a wee spot of bother and I need someone to sort it out. A fellow from up the Shankill owes me a few quid and well it's the usual story, 'I'll give it to you next week' and he keeps putting me back."

"Who is he?"

"I only know him by his nickname, Pinky, but he's the usual; has a bet and knocks you, then punts away with another bookie."

"So what can I do about it?" Jimmy and Silver enter into deep conversation and Jimmy buys Silver another drink and gets up to leave. "Dunmore Park tonight about half seven. I'll see you there. You can walk in with me. It won't cost you a light."

That night, at precisely half past seven, Silver is standing in the brightly lit car park of Dunmore Park. When Jimmy drives by him and hails him over to the car. "Here, you carry my bookies bag in and they will think you're working for me and save you paying in." Silver grabs the bag and follows Jimmy and both walk in. As the crowd starts to come in, Jimmy tells Silver that he will point Pinky out and if he starts punting with another bookie Silver can pull him.

After the second race Pinky shows and Jimmy nods to Silver to keep an eye on him. Pinky is a big rangy guy, wiry and tall. Silver eyes him up but he needs to feel him out, so he pushes through the crowd to where Pinky is standing with a few of his friends and bumps into him purposely and walks away, after apologising. Just then Pinky walks over and has a bet with Jackie Thomas.

Jimmy makes eyes at Silver. Silver walks over to Jimmy and tells him to wait and see if the bet touches. He explains, "When he's collecting his winnings, if he doesn't approach you to pay up, I will give him a tug. It's no use pulling him if the bet's beat, so we will play it by ear."

Trap six the winner is announced over the public address and Pinky comes walking in shoulders out, like most gamblers when they have bet a winner and walks straight to Jacky Thomas.

Silver walks over to Pinky and asks can he have a word and Pinky asks him about what.

"Well, it's like this lad. I work for Jimmy Connolly and you owe him two hundred quid and not only are you not paying him but you're punting with another bookie. Do you think that's fair? At least give him some of what you owe him. He was decent enough to let you have credit, so act the wise man." Pinky looks at Silver, then looks around him and nods to a couple of his friends and they walk over and surround Silver. "So you're going to be a big fellow and create a rumpus, now that you're team handed." says Silver.

"Who do you think you are, coming over to me and asking me for money and putting the bounce on me? Now fuck off before I knock you into next week whoever you are and count yourself lucky I'm in a good mood! Now fuck off!"

Silver moves back and by this time a crowd had gathered around the men. Silver asks Pinky out to the car park. Suddenly Pinky throws a haymaker at Silver. It makes Silver fall back a little but he always does this to gather his thoughts. Then he immediately throws off his coat and before long has Pinky on the ground. All Pinky's pals jump on. The crowd is cheering for Silver and some of the crowd is backing Pinky and his mates. Silver is getting beaten to a pulp when a man pushes his way through the crowd. It's none other than Stormy Weatherall who jumps in and knocks two of Pinky's mates clean out. He then pulls Pinky and Silver apart and declares a fair fight and he will make sure no one jumps on. Pinky and Silver square up to each other and the crowd is baying for blood. Silver steps forward, tip toes to the side and bang one punch on the chin and its all over. Pinky is out cold. After a few minutes Pinky comes around and Stormy grabs him in front of the crowd and tells him that he let the Shankill Road down, fighting Silver mob handed.

"What's it all about anyway, Paddy?"

"He owes Jimmy Connolly a few quid and he's been ignoring him for months and punting with other bookies. Jimmy just asked me to give him a wee reminder."

"Now if I were you Pinky, I'd go over and make some deal with Jimmy or you will have me to deal with, never mind Silver."

Pinky is flabbergasted, "You mean that was Silver McKee I was fighting." Stormy nods in the affirmative. "God, I'm sorry Silver. Can I shake your hand?" Silver and Pinky shake hands and Pinky says there is no problem. "I will square Jimmy up, over the next few weeks, honest."

"You better!" says Stormy "and I'd start by giving him something tonight." Pinky dusts himself down walks over to Jimmy's pitch and hands him some money. "Jimmy, you didn't have to go that far. Silver McKee of all men! I've heard so much about him, he's a real tough man." Silver is standing talking to Stormy when Jimmy walks over from his pitch and hands Silver a few pounds and says, "Take your friend for a drink you both deserve it." Jimmy tries to hand Stormy the price of a drink and he refuses profusely to accept it. "No chance but I might have a wee knock bet with you some night."

"Not a problem. Any friend of Silvers is a friend of mine. By the way do you want to go to point to point next week Paddy? You'll get a days pay."

"If I don't have anything else on, I'll be there. I think we deserve that drink now Stormy.

Let's go over to the Elsinore. I want to tell that story you were asking about."

"You mean the one about the counterfeit money."

"Yes, that one. I still haven't got to the bottom of it yet, but I will someday.

"Let it go. It will only eat away at you. The rest of the fellows involved in it don't give a damn," says Stormy.

The next morning Silver awakens from his armchair in the living room and Mary is fixing the babies nappy. Silver asks her the time.

"I'll tell you what time it is, it's time I wasn't here. I've had enough of your drunken loutish behaviour. Another night of it coming home and bringing your arguments home with you."

"I wasn't arguing with anyone."

"Well you could have fooled me. All you talked about in your drunken stupor was about somebody called Pinky. I know Stormy, who you went on and on about. You done nothing but talk about both of them. Well I've had enough of it. I'm going to my mums. And I heard you have a new name or name's should I say. The bread server or the strikebreaker; which do you prefer? Sure that woman next door couldn't hold her water. She told the whole district about the loaves."

"I'm going to kill that Cheeky Charlie when I get him. He told me you were out and he left them next door."

"When do I ever go out? He just got rid of the loaves as fast as he could so he could chase after a few bob but anyway who could blame him. He's not your message boy."

"Look Mary, my head's bursting. Would you quit going on and on. You're like an old dog with a bone."

"Yes, I know and I'm beginning to look and feel like one and that's the end of it. You can listen to someone else. I'm going, Paddy, so you will be free to do as you please. And on that note you always done what you pleased. Never once did you buy me a present. Anne is near a year old and you haven't bought her one thing – not even a new pair of shoes."

"I'll give you a week at that farmhouse of your ma's. It would freeze you and the toilet up the field, for Christ's sake. Catch yourself on. You don't know when your well off, wee girl."

"Well I'm fed up running after you, lifting and laying you. It's not a wife you want Paddy, it's a slave."

"Would you quit now, Mary my heads splitting. I'm going to the pub. If you're here when I get back, so be it, if not well good luck to you but let me tell you, you had better look after that child of mine."

"There you go again. Everything is yours. Your house, your money, your child your splitting, frigging head. Well I've had an enough of 'me, me, and me.' I'm looking after us two from now on. Anne and me. So you can lump it or leave it."

"Sometimes woman, I wish you where a man."

"What! So you could hit me a punch on the face and act the big hard man."

Silver gets up and puts on his coat and slams the door on his way out. Mary burst out crying and roars at the top of her voice, "Men, whoever invented men?"

Next morning Silver awakens to the sound of the postman putting something through the letterbox. He jumps up and calls for Mary to lift the post in the hall but there's no response. "Mary! The post is in the hall," he roars but no reply. So he gets out of the chair and walks to the hall and lifts some envelopes and places them on the table and runs up the stairs. "Mary! Where the hell are you?" He runs back down the stairs and sits down on his chair and ponders his future. He now realises that Mary has left and he's on his own. Just at that, the hall door is being knocked and he gets up and peeps through the window muttering, "That will be her back," but it's big McCausland. As Silver opens the door to him, McCausland says he needs to talk to him right away. Silver invites him in and both sit at the table and Silver is looking at the envelopes sitting on the table.

"We have to go to court next week."

"What for? I've seen enough of courts to do me a lifetime and there's no way

I'm going back to court – win lose or draw."

"I think if you open that brown envelope you may change your mind."

"What brown envelope?"

"The one sitting in front of you. "It looks official and I got one similar to it this morning. It's a summons but it's for a different court. Harry is taking me to court to take possession of my house and we are called as witnesses."

"But what's it got to do with me? I don't own the house."

"Fuck me Silver! Do you not care about anyone only yourself. I'm losing my family home and you're wondering what it's got to do with you. Don't you remember you were there when the deal was done and when the real money turned into counterfeit."

"How could I forget it? Didn't I do three months in Her Majesty's big house? And it wasn't Buckingham palace let me tell you. I lost near a stone in weight when I was in there and I'm not going back."

"Look listen for a minute. Open that letter and you may understand it more. It's not a criminal court, it's a civil action taken by that bastard Robinson to take my home." Silver is a bit reluctant to open the envelope, but after a few moments he opens it and starts reading aloud, "You are hereby summoned to appear at the master of the Rolls on Friday at ten o'clock in the forenoon. Failure to appear will result in you being arrested and brought before the courts to explain your actions. Who do these people think they are?"

"I'll tell you who they are. Do you know big Bob and Jim who are in the variety market every Friday. Well that's who they are? Judges and barristers and solicitors. They're the real law in this town and they decide what goes."

"So what do they want with me?

"I need to get my four grand back and Harry wants his ten."

"So what's the problem then?"

"The problem is or was that two grand was counterfeit money. He says it's not his and it definitely wasn't mine."

"Well you can be sure of one thing and that's not two, it wasn't mine. So who owned it or better still who put it in the case? You where with me at all times and the only one I can think of is that wee Tom fellow. Didn't we stop at your house so you could go in and get more of your money on the way to the hotel? That's been on my mind for a while and I was wondering did you do a switch?"

"For heaven's sake catch yourself on. My son's life was at stake. Do you think I'm going to give somebody Mickey Mouse money and risk his life for Gods sake? Have you no brains man?"

"I'm the only one who went to jail and I got nothing out of it and nobody came looking me when I got out. I got sacked from the markets and I've never had it so bad in all my life. Not only that, Mary's gone and you're asking me have I no brains."

"Look you know what I mean. It's just a figure of speech but somebody's going to the wall for two grand and its not going to be me. If I can prove that it was Harry then I will get my house back according to my barrister. So you better forget that I went to my house after we left him. All you have to say is that the money was in your possession from Harry's house until you got to the hotel."

"That's all fine and dandy but what's in it for me?"

"I'll give you a monkey if I get my deeds back and that's a promise."

"Can you talk English? What's a monkey?"

"Five hundred quid. That should cover you for being in jail and I will be happy getting my real money back. More importantly keeping my house. Oh, one other thing. We have to walk over to the court on Thursday to meet my brief and all you tell him is what I've said to you and Bob's your uncle."

"Aye and Fanny's your aunt. I'll have to think about all this. Wonder what Harry's offering?"

"You wouldn't take sides with him, would you Silver?"

"I found out something when I was in jail. Money talks. I'm going up the Falls to see two men and then I will give you my answer."

"And who may they be?"

"Well it's really none of your business but one of them is Pa Jordon and the other would be Comanche."

"Who are they – a cowboy and an Indian?"

"No. Just two of the shrewdest men in this town. Lets say they're bar room lawyers that know the score. They won't be looking anything from me in return. What's that old saying that's doing the rounds now – they owe me one."

"Your wasting your time. I'm working with a barrister."

"I know all that but your barrister is a legal brain but he hasn't got street savvy and he wouldn't know where forged money came from but I guarantee these pair if they don't know where it came from you can bet that they know someone who does."

"Good luck to you but please be there on Thursday. It's only round the corner from your house. I will call for you."

"You can call all you want. I may be going with Harry. You never know. I'm too old of a cat to be bucked by a kitten and I'm fed up with everybody and everyone. So for a change Silver is looking after himself."

"Have you gone mad McKee?"

"No. I've come to my senses. I've worked in the cattle market since I was a boy, now I'm not allowed on the premises and you're asking me if I'm mad. I think it's my time now. No more messing. I think a lot of people have forgotten. This is Silver's city."

* * *

Thursday comes along and Silver decides that he would go to the court as it's literally on his doorstep. So it's not a big problem for him. He puts on his best suit and a nice clean shirt and tie and his best brown boots. As he's fixing his long flowing blonde hair in the mirror, he starts rehearsing what he's going to tell Billy and Harry and then what he will reveal to the judge. He looks at the clock – it's nine o'clock. He pours himself a cup of tea and sits down feeling rather pleased with himself. There is a loud knocking at the front door. "Who's there?" he shouts. "It's me, Billy McCausland. We haven't much time. Are you ready?"

"Come in, the front doors open."

Billy walks in and looks at Silver. "Where are you going to, a funeral?"

"No but I'm not going to look like a gobshite as you and Harry prance about in your flashy suits. You see my friends up the Falls told me a few things and one of them was this. When you go to court dress like a business man and the judge will look fairer upon you while he's working out whether you're telling the truth or lying."

"Good advice but we have got to be going. I'm meeting my barrister at half nine and if I'm not there he won't wait. Time is money. Let's get going."

Silver stands up and Harry looks him up and down. "Not a bad turn out for a cattle drover. You could pass for a big time builder but lets get over to the court and see what he has to say because its him that will be doing most of the talking." The two men walk out the front door into the street and walk briskly down the street. On arrival in the court halls, Billy's barrister is standing in his silks with a pile of papers under his arm. He approaches Billy and beckons him into a café inside the court. Billy orders three teas.

"No, I will have a coffee," chirps the barrister. After getting the tea and coffee the men settle down to talk about the case. "I'm Bob Saunders QC and I'm representing Mr. McCausland and I presume you are Mr. McKee."

"Yes, that's me. Patrick Joseph McKee and I only live across the road in that wee district called the Market."

"I know all about you Sir. Your name precedes you and I have seen you on the occasional Friday when I was in the markets buying some fresh fish. So I have to ask you one thing Sir. Was the counterfeit money yours?" Silver stands up and looks at Bob.

"I hope your joking if you think I play with counterfeit money. I'm a man of my word. Ask anyone."

Billy tells Silver to sit down and Bob tells him in no uncertain terms that he has to ask the question as a matter of course. "I'm not inferring anything but that's my job and if you are not going to cooperate we may be wasting our time here. You see Mr. McKee or should I call you by your street name and address you as Silver. It may make you feel more comfortable but remember this. I was born on the Shankill Road and there's one sure thing in life. You can take the boy out of the Falls, the Market, or the Shankill, but you can't take the birthplace out of the boy. Now if we are to continue can you sit down as I have a case at ten thirty and time is of the essence?"

Silver sits down a bit reluctantly and Billy asks him to just listen and answer the questions and not interrupt. Bob asks Silver again but uses different words, "Did you own any of the money that the court has taken charge of?"

"Can I ask you a question Mr. Saunders?"

"Yes. Go ahead."

"If I went to jail for possession of the money that is being held by the court would that not mean I own it.?"

"Billy, I don't know why your employing me. I think Silver knows a bit about the law. Maybe he should be representing you." Silver and Billy laugh but Bob gets a bit resentful and is fuming.

"Forget about that. He's just being funny."

"Well this is no laughing matter. If we start a legal charge over the money and you say its yours, Harry says it's his and then Silver takes a charge on it, we're up shit creek to put it mildly. I'm going to ask for an adjournment tomorrow so you need not attend and the next time we meet can I have my instruction from you Mr McCausland. Aren't you paying the bills?" Bob gets up and turns to both men on his way out and says, "Next time come on your own and we may get something done. I'm not here to be made a fool of. This is no laughing matter."

"Look what you've done now for God's sake. Could you not have kept your mouth shut and let the man talk."

"Do you want to know something, you big fat fucker, I'm not listening to anyone any more. Not you or that idiot dressed up like batman. I'm my own man from here on in and I will be saying my piece. Now I'm away to get drunk and if you have anything else to say, say it now, or forever hold your peace. Don't be coming over to the Black Bull because let me tell you if I get a few drinks in me I'm not going to be in the best of form." Silver gets up and walks out leaving Billy bewildered and sitting holding his head in his hands.

* * *

The bread strike is now in its final hours, as the union led by John McCann, Shakie's uncle, is deliberating with the bosses of English's bakery in the nearby primary school. The room is packed with bakers; fancy bread men van drivers and general labourers. They are arguing over an eight shilling a week rise and a ten-shilling rise is what the union is fighting for. The room is buzzing when a door opens and in walks Silver along side Trevor. The room comes to an abrupt silence and everyone turns to look at Silver and Trevor. The chairman of the meeting tells both men to take a chair so the meeting can continue without interruption. John McCann walks back to Silver and asks him what he's playing at.

"This is my friend Trevor, who is a delegate in your union and I thought he might be able to help you in some way." Trevor flashes his union card and John smiles, "Anyone from the union is welcome here, so take a seat please and give us your support." The three men sit down and the meeting goes on but is not going anywhere with people shouting and others stomping there feet.

Silver gets to his feet and asks for quiet. "I've brought my good friend Trevor down here from the Shankill Road and he's willing to help negotiate on your behalf."

Someone shouts from the crowd, "Why? Are we not capable of looking after ourselves? Do you think we are stupid?" John McCann gets up and tells the floor that Trevor is a delegate and has every right to be there no matter where he is from. "He is a union brother. Let him speak."

Trevor gets to his feet and starts by introducing himself to his fellow brothers of the union. He explains that it may be a jump too far for management to give the ten shilling rise and if they took the eight shilling rise with a view to a review in six months time it may be easier for the management to swallow. John jumps to his feet and tells the crowd that this was the best suggestion he had heard all day and it was worth consideration. He would like to take it to a vote. Trevor interrupts and tells John and the crowd that a lot of things need changed but what is needed most is for the men to get back to work, as the country is on its knees with no bread, the staple diet and he would gladly help in any other way to redress the situation in the bakery. He also would like to thank Silver for inviting him along. Someone shouts, "Who? the bread server?" Silver gets up off his seat to see who was shouting but Trevor tells him to sit down. After a bit of consultation the management agrees to an eight shilling a week rise and a review in six months and they will look at conditions such as sick pay and other requests from the union. The vote is put to the floor and to a man it is accepted unanimously and the crowd starts clapping. After the din has died down a man gets on his feet and asks for three cheers for John McCann and Trevor and most of all Silver for bringing him to the meeting. The crowd cheer very enthusiastically and Trevor looks at Silver and smiles. Then whispers in his ear. "Redemption my friend. Never turn your back on your people. Let the red flag fly and one day we will be a united people, first and foremost, and not slaves to the capitalistic world."

Within minutes of the strike being over, the word has raced around the market that Silver ended the strike and the men will be back to work in days; an exaggeration of course but Belfast is a town like that. Always looking for the good side in people and that's how folklore begins and stays with us forever. Big John McCann who worked in the bakery for most of his life didn't end it or Trevor the wee man from the Shankill. No it was again that man, the Belfast man with a real heart of gold, just like his hair, Silver McKee.

Silver and Trevor are walking through the market and a man called Stack stops him and tells Silver that there's a big cockney man wants to talk to him about setting up a business in the area. Silver asks him what has it got to do with him and Stack tells him that he's marrying his sister and he wants a little help just to get going. Trevor looks at Silver and reminds him about his own people and to watch what he is doing as he is now back being the good fellow. Another back stab like the bread sale could finish him in the area. Silver cant resist the thought that someone from London is looking his help and he asks Stack what is his name. "He's called John Walshe and he's a big lump of a guy but the bottom line is he's got money and brains and he wants to work in the area."

"Look, Trevor and me are going for a drink in the Black Bull so if he wants to talk to me I will be there." Stacks nods in agreement and walks off.

"You will have to get a proper office Paddy. The public house doesn't become you." Both men laugh as they walk through the doors of the pub and are met by a large crowd who are quick to shake hands with both men in a congratulatory way. Big John McCann pushes through the crowd and asks

Trevor for his hand and tells him he has a great way with words and is a good union man. Trevor is flustered as big John asks him and Silver what they'd like to drink.

Chapter 7

The next morning Silver wakes up on what now has become his bed, the settee in the living room. As he rubs his face and runs his hands through his hair he goes searching for a drink about the house and sits down and calls out, "There's never a drink in this house when you need one." Drink is no longer for enjoyment or relaxation for Silver. It's slowly becoming a necessity for which he has no longer any power over. "I'll have to get off this drink. It's killing me," he says to himself as he shuffles around the house looking his shoes. He kicks the chair in a rage and then throws himself on the settee and has another sleep in despair.

Someone is knocking on the door and Silver gets up, goes to the window and draws the curtain only to see Billy McCausland standing outside. "That's all I need. Him coming here talking a load of bollocks about how the courts work and his big house. If I had the air of them words I could sing them." Silver opens the door and lets Billy in and both men walk into the living room.

Billy looks around him and moves a bundle of clothing of a chair and sits down. "I only came here to tell you that court case has been put off to the winter assizes so you have nothing to worry about, at least for a while."

"Why should I have anything to worry about? I've done my time and I'm not going back to jail for man, woman nor beast."

"Well I see your getting along well, living on your own," utters Billy sarcastically. "No sign of the wife coming back?"

"She'll be back when she finds out what side her breads buttered on. Stuck up on that oul farm in Castlereagh."

"Well I'm away here. I've a few things to do around Allams; buy a few heifers that I have an order for."

"Tell me big man, could you lend me a tenner out of that ferret or gorilla you promised me if the court case goes well for you?"

"Ha, ha! You mean a monkey. That's the best I ever heard. A gorilla! A tenner that's a weeks wages for most men around here and they don't grow on trees. Can I ask what you want it for?"

"Look, either loan me it or be on your way. Remember I hold all the aces in the court case.

So if I was you I'd look favourably on my request."

"Who has been educating you? You're starting to sound like a real wide boy who knows all the answers."

"Look it's simple. I need a few quid and if you can't give me it I know someone who will, without a cough."

Billy pulls out a wad of notes from his trouser pocket and peels a fiver off, "That's enough to get some food in and plenty left to get you drunk. I am not lending you it, lets say it's an investment and I don't want it back." Billy bids Silver good luck and walks out the door. Silver hurries himself and gets dressed, washes his face, and makes his way out of the house. On his way up the street he meets Croaky.

"Morning, Croaky, how are things going at the markets?"

"I haven't been back since big Sam warned me off. Well he sent me over to tell you that you are welcome back next week. He heard what you done for the bakers and he knows if there's no work around here, the markets will crumble. So you get yourself straightened out and you can start back on Monday."

"Great news Croaky but who will be running the show you or me?"

"We shall cross that bridge when we come to it. I'm not that foolish to not know that when you come back the men will only take orders from one person."

"And who would that be Croaky?"

"You." Croaky turns and walks away stops and turns back. "It wouldn't be a bad idea for you to go up and see Mary. At least you'll get a clean shirt everyday, if nothing else."

"What are you on about?" cries Silver?"

"Go back to the house and have a look in the mirror for God's sake and all our sakes. Get a grip of yourself." Silver mutters a mouthful of obscenities as he danders down the street and then he stops. A bus is coming down Cromac Street and Silver waves it down at the bus stop, boards it and takes a seat.

The conductor is shouting "Fares please!" and he comes to Silver. "Fare sir." Silver pulls out the fiver an old trick he learned from Joe Hughes but in reality it's all he has. Joe runs a yard that lends out horses and carts to hawkers who gather scrap, rags, or wastepaper.

"A four dee to the Grosvenor road, please." Silver hands the conductor the five-pound note and the conductor looks at him.

"Is that the smallest you have Silver?"

"I'm afraid so, son. Do I know you?"

"I don't think so but I know you. It's okay this time, but if the inspector gets on you can tell him you threw your ticket away. He won't argue with you especially if he knows who you are." Silver laughs. A couple of stops later and Silver is getting off the bus and the conductor says to him, "That's the oldest trick in the book. Getting on a bus with a fiver."

"Look son, it's all I have between me and the man above, so help me I swear. I'll get you the next time I'm on the bus. I will pay you double."

"Ah and pigs might fly." Silver dismounts the bus and waves at the conductor as the bus pulls away. Silver walks across the road and heads for Servia Street where Joe's yard is situated. He stoops down and walks through the wicket gate into what can only described as a small farmyard right in the middle of the Falls Road district. Joe sees Silver coming and walks up and greets him with a strong handshake.

"What has you up in this neck of the woods, Paddy?"

"I came up to see you and ask when are you going to the Puck Fair and who's doing the driving?"

"We're leaving on the Friday; me, Hack Kerr and big Kane."

"So there's room for me?"

"You'll have to sort it out with Henry. He owns the car but I'm sure it will be all right as Jimmy Mackie isn't going, so I think you'd be all right for the seat. But I'd advise you to walk down to Kane's yard and make arrangements with him. You know what he's like. He likes everyone to be there on the button. Doesn't like hanging about."

"I know. He hasn't a minute since he went off that oul drink. It's rush, rush, rush. He drives that big Vauxhall like it's a racing car. Suppose while I'm up this far I can walk down to his yard and have a yarn with him. See what's what."

Joe says to Paddy, "I haven't seen you in a while. What's been happening with you?"

"Well you know I was in jail over the head of those other two-fuck pots but they'll pay. They think they're very clever using me like a stupid schoolboy."

"Look Paddy, I'd just walk down and book your seat, just in case you never know who'll want to go to the Puck. It is one of the best fairs of the year. In fact there's a lot of young lads from around here going, so some of them will be looking a lift down maybe." "Troublemakers Joe?

"No all good lads but a bit wild. You wouldn't know them. Fellows called Fra Ward, Jim Haughey and Go Go Riley and of course Lazy Tom but I think he's going in a different car along with Jacky McBurney and Bud Dorrian and some other lads."

"I know the Wards. His brother Jimmy was a pal of mine. Aren't they from Osman Street?" "That's the ones."

"Where'd the other boy Go Go get that name?"

"Well it's like every thing else. He got called it after another Go Go that ran about the yard here. But they're good lads; only hope they don't go drinking down at the Puck, what with all the fighting men that go. Boyos trying to make a name for themselves. Wouldn't want any trouble. I hope that big guy Bronco isn't there looking a return you know."

"Joe my fighting days are over."

"Yes, we know you don't want to be fighting but the young lads see it as a feather in their cap if they fight the great Silver McKee."

"I'll dander on down and see big Henry and book my seat."

Just at that Joe's nephew, Yacko Hughes walks into the yard and walks over to Silver.

"Are you going to the Puck, Paddy?"

"I think so son. I'm on my way down to Kane's yard to book my seat in the car."

"Can I walk down with you?"

"Come on ahead. You'll be company. I'm not too sure of my way around here, so you can show me the way down." Silver and Yacko leave the yard and walk down a few streets and they are outside Kane's yard on Albert Street.

"Oh, I know where I am now son; I'm going in to see big Kane. Good luck." Silver walks up the yard and Yacko sits himself down on the kerb outside the yard. As Silver walks up the yard he meets Hack Kerr, Maurice McCorry, and Jim O'Reilly, not to be confused with Go Go but neighbours of each other. Hack takes Silver aside and asks him is he going to the Puck and Silver tells him that he's up to see big Kane for a lift. Hack walks him down to the office and big Kane is sprawled out in front of a roaring fire half asleep. Hack lets a roar out of him and awakens Henry. When he sees Silver he gets up and shakes his hand. "I haven't been up to see you since I got out of jail but I'm here now and you done me a big favour. Now I need another one, I need a lift to the puck.

Kane ponders for a minute. "Is Jimmy Mackie definitely not going Hack? He's going down with his son Bobby who's just got his licence. Jimmy bought him a car. More the fool. Wouldn't be me."

"He's not a bad lad, Hack."

"I know but he's too fond of the drink and I wouldn't be sitting in a car with him. Okay Paddy, next Friday at the corner of Cromac Street, half eight and I mean half eight and be sober. I'm not long off the drink and I don't want to be listening to a drunk man."

"The jobs a goodun. I will take a dander up and see big Dan Fenton. Haven't seen him in a while."

"Well first things first. He is away on the boats and have you heard the latest? He's immigrating to Australia."

"Your joking Henry! Dan going to Australia?"

"That's right," says Hack. He's got his tickets paid for and when he comes back from this trip, Lizzie and him are going."

"That's a sad state of affairs," sighs Silver. "I'm going up the yard to say hello to a couple of your workers and I won't be yarning all day to them. I know they have to work. Then I'm off home."

"What about you and Mary?" asks Kane

"She's up in her ma's. Good enough for her."

"That's not the attitude Paddy. When we come back from the Puck try and make it up with her."

"I will. Now I'm away. It's Friday morning nine o'clock, at the corner of Cromac Street?" "Half eight and don't be late."

Silver walks out of the office and up the yard and has a yarn with Maurice and young Jim and then he walks down the yard and on to Albert Street where Yacko is sitting waiting. "Would you fancy going for a pint Paddy?"

"I don't mind but I'm only going for one and I mean one, just to be sociable."

"We'll go up to the Decent Mans."

"Where's that?"

"Sean McGeown's. It's just at the top of the street." Silver and Yacko head up Albert Street and Yacko is asking Silver question after question about dealing, fighting and jail.

"You seem to know a lot about me son. Are you writing a book?" Yacko looks at him in amazement and really doesn't know what he's talking about. On entering the Decent Mans they approach the bar and take a stool each. Sean McGeown walks out from behind the bar.

"Did I not tell you that you were barred from here only last week, Yacko?" "No. You told me not to come back for a fortnight." "Do you know this lad, mister?" asks Sean.

"I know he's Joe Hughes nephew and I am only having one pint with him and I'm going home."

"Okay, one pint for you Yacko. You can stay as long as you like and let this be your last warning." After he quickly finishes his pint, Yacko bids Silver good luck and heads out the door. Silver counts his tank; four pounds six shilling, so he orders another pint and a halfun when Danny Braniff pops into the bar. Danny at once walks over to Silver and shakes hands with him. Danny knows everyone and used to work for Kane but got paid off about a month previous. "Didn't see you in the yard today Danny. I was asking about you."

"I've got the best job in the country now Paddy. I'm working for Hunters Drinks Company.

You know the old saying 'Hunters stout is sticking out.' " Both men laugh.

"Did you and Kane fall out again over something stupid?"

"No there's no work. Maurice is going to be next unless the scrap trade picks up. He hasn't been doing anything since he moved to Albert Street. None of the hawkers are selling to him." "Why's that Danny?"

"The way I worked it out, they don't like sorting their chugs and scrap on the main street and Albert Street is the main street up here. It and the Grosvenor Road. Probably in case some dole man sees them, but it's not everyone who wants people to see that they are hawkers. Funny nobody gives them anything, so why worry."

"Bit of pride Danny. Every body has some form of it. Danny orders a drink and Silver pays for it. After a few sips Danny says he is going to the bookies to have a bet and tells Silver he got a tip for horse. "What do you call it Danny?"

"Stoneyford Jack and I was told it wouldn't be beat."

"Here have me a pound on it. On the nose or each way. Whatever way you do it; sure I don't back horses. I'm just doing it because you got a tip for the horse." Danny takes the pound and heads out the door. A few minutes later he returns with a big broad smile on his face and hands silver six pounds. Silver rubs his hands and orders both men a drink. After a few hours drinking Danny tells him that he feels his luck is in and is heading to the Shotts, a gambling club where they play Faro, a very fast game and definitely not for beginners. Silver asks him if he can tag along and Danny and him head up the road.

Inside the Shotts there are two snooker tables, a potbelly stove and a room where no young people are allowed. A wee man who is very well dressed is the manager or the marker up, as he is better known. Simmy, as he is called wears flamboyant ties and nice bright suits and is always on his toes to stop any trouble that may occur between the gamblers. Silver and Danny walk into the Faro room and it is packed with men gambling away and some who are just looking on, hoping that someone will give them a start so they can join in. Silver asks Danny how the game is played. Danny tells him to watch for a few hands and all he has to remember is that the second card is the winner. And if the same two cards say like two jacks come out you loose half your stake. Silver is scratching his head as Danny folds a ten bob note and sets it on the marker board and calls half way on the jack. That means, he tells Silver that he has only five bob on so if it was a pound note and you only wanted to bet five bob and you call it and set the pound on the corner. Silver pulls a pound note out of his pocket and throws it on the jack following Danny and after a few turns, seven then jack comes up and Silver and Danny both win. After about an hour Silver is winning about twenty quid when the banker packs in.

"How could you beat those two lucky bastards. I've done my money to two mugs."

"I wouldn't like to think you're talking about me, big lad," says Silver. "We put our money down and won. What's the big deal?"

"I'll tell you what it is if I give you a broken jaw." Silver has never been in the Shotts before and none of the guys really know who he is. But one guy knows him. That's Mickey The Hard.

Mickey got this name because he knew all the hard men but he wasn't a fighter himself.

"Gerry, you're backing a loser. If I was you I would go on home and forget about it," says Mickey.

"Forget about it. I just lost forty quid and your asking me to lap it."

"I'm not asking you to do anything Gerry. I'm just saying to go on home and I think you'd be far better off."

"Mind you your own business. You're nothing but a slabber." All the while Silver is counting his money and a few guys gather round him asking him for a start or a couple of shilling to get into the next game.

"I'm not finished yet boys. Let's see how I go later. I might divide a few bob between youse."

Simmy comes marching into the room. "What's the problem? Whose is bidding for the bank?" This is the formula used to decide the next banker and who ever bids the most gets to be banker but he must show the amount he bids. A young guy called O'Hara bids twenty quid and Simmy hands him the cards. So the game settles down, and play resumes under the new banker Brendan O'Hara. O'Hara is like lightening drawing the cards and has been known to draw a few seconds which actually means drawing the second card first with slight of hand. As the game goes on big Gerry is still slabbering when Jimmy O'Hare walks into the room and walks straight over to Silver.

"What's the trouble?" asks Jimmy.

"Nothing I can't handle myself. That young lad seems to think you're not allowed to win."

Just at that Gerry jumps up and says "Let's have you outside now mister! You come up here acting as if you're stupid and can't play. Who do you think we are, mugs?"

Silver lifts his money off the card table and answers Gerry. "I'm your man. In fact anyone here wants to have a fair go, I'm their man as well." Jimmy O'Hare who knows Silver well asks him to head on home and not to let that mouth piece Gerry in the corner mess him about.

"Look Silver don't mind him," says Jimmy.

Silver say, "I'm not going to go on home and everyone should settle down. I'll go home after a few more hands." Gerry is surprised and now knows who Silver is. He jumps up and walks out with his head held down. All the faces are there now in the Shotts, and it is buzzing. There's Patsy, beat you like a dog Nolan, Geordie Caddel, Joe Hennessy, Mundo O'Rawe, Joe McCullough, Peezer Ward, and Rab Walsh, Eamon Heaney, and Frog Mooney. The money is changing hands fast and furious and Silver is winning.

"That's me!" calls Silver. "Are you staying Dan?"

"No I'm coming with you." As Silver is about to leave someone shouts, "What's the initials of Vic Oliver!?" and this is a sign for a VO, where everyone dives on the table and they fight over the money which doesn't even belong to them. Silver still has a pound on the table. Silver grabs his pound note and lifts the large table up and turns it on its side.

"What sort of a place is this?" As he is walking out, down a long narrow hallway, he walks into near total darkness and he feels a punch on the jaw. Silver shakes his head, moves back, and looks at his assailant. It's big Gerry. Silver is now surrounded by all of the guys who were in the card room and Simmy is telling him he's barred.

"Don't worry when I sort your man out here I'm barring myself." Silver hands Danny his coat and squares up to big Gerry who is fit but no match for Silver. Silver grabs him, holds him tight and batters away at his rib cage. As Gerry is slipping down after all the body punches Silver pulls him up on his feet and plants a right hook flush on his jaw. It's all over. Silver gets his coat off Danny and asks the crowd, "Is there anyone one else wants to try and make a name for themselves?" No one replies and Silver shouts, "I thought so!" Danny and him walk out.

Chapter 8

Belfast fair day has come around again and it is busier than usual as the rumors are flying around that this may be the last year of the fair and the cattle sales yard. Silver walks into the square. There are a hundred or so horses tied to Allams wall: and others tied to the back of horse boxes; some being trotted up and down to try and catch the eye of prospective buyers; Shetland ponies and Welsh cobs. Several trotters, each yoked in a sulky, are racing up and down the square.

The first man Silver meets is Croaky.

"I told you to start back on Monday, Silver. So what's it to be? It's not like the old days now where you done what you wanted. Times are changing."

"Look, leave it to next week. I will start on Monday. I've so much on my mind and when I get it all sorted out I will be here Monday morning at nine o'clock guaranteed."

"Okay, but don't be letting me down. The men are wondering what's going on and asking is there a deal being done behind their backs."

"Look, Croaky, as I told you, I need to sort Mary and the child out. Get her back home and then I will get stuck in and try and sort this mess out. Look around you. How long has it been since you seen a crowd at the horse fair? I haven't seen a crowd like this for years."

"Neither have I Paddy but the truth is they think it's the last."

"Over my dead body. This is the life's blood of the Market. Look," Silver points, "the abattoir down there, the potato market over there, the fruit and veg on the far side and the fish market behind me. Do you really think this is all going to close?"

"Do you want an honest answer Paddy?"

"Yes I do and nothing you or me will be able to do anything about it."

Silver spots big McCausland and walks over to have a word. Silver pulls him aside. "Any word on that court case coming off because I'm sick of it all."

"Your sick of it. I'm sitting on eggs while that bastard Robinson has the deeds of my house and my money."

"Well that's not correct. The court has it all."

"But if they find in his favour I'm finished and homeless. That's worry Paddy. Not where the next drink is coming from."

"That's a problem you can solve."

"I can't solve this one as the judge is going to call another adjournment and the longer it goes on the longer I can't move."

"I understand, big man but I have to look after my own troubles and at the minute it's getting Mary back. I was never cut out for living on my own, ironing shirts and making grub. I'm useless I haven't hands to bless myself." Silver walks away and shouts back, "Get that barrister to get the hurry up on that case. I'm thinking of going away." As Silver is walking from Billy he bumps into Walter Cunningham an old horse dealer whose son is also called Walter and are referred to as old and young Walter.

"Hello Paddy, I haven't seen you about in weeks. You hiding from us all?"

"Sure I don't owe you anything, do I Walter?"

"Now you know that I didn't mean that Paddy. What's wrong with you? I've never asked you for money in my life."

"I'm sorry Walter. I'm in a terrible mood. Everything I touch goes wrong."

"Well you walked yourself into jail. You should have told on whoever set you up. Because as sure as there is a God in heaven, you where set up."

"Do you think so Walter?"

"I don't think so, I know so! It's the talk of the Markets and they're even taking bets on who put the counterfeit money in the case. I don't know what you're doing running after that big McCausland. He's no good and never was."

"How do you work that out?"

"Simple." Walter calls his son over and he immediately shakes hands with Silver and welcomes him back. "Answer me one question, son. Who do you think put the dummy money in the case?"

"Well, I'll take odds of two to one it was Billy because he's the sleekitist big man in this whole crowd."

"But that doesn't make him the one. I need hard evidence."

"Any man that buys another mans cattle and doesn't pay for them is no good. Do you see anyone with him. He's a loner and as far as I'm concerned you're a man of your word like us or you're no good."

"Look I get where your coming from but I was just doing a job for him and it was his only son. Do you think he would do a thing like that?"

"It's back to the old saying Paddy, desperate men do desperate things and sometimes very stupid things."

What do you think Walter?"

"I agree with my Da but I have a few horses to sell so I will talk to you later and don't be bringing the old man over to that Black Bull and getting him drunk."

"Sure I wouldn't do a thing like that now would I?" Walter senior winks at Silver as young Walter, steel liner whip in hand, walks back to try and sell a few horses. Silver danders on down the markets after telling Walter senior that he would meet him in the pub about three o'clock but in the meantime he has some work to do. The funny thing about the two Cunninghams is that young Walter doesn't smoke in front of his Da, even though he is over thirty and Walter senior won't drink in front of his son and he's over sixty. It's just the way it is and sometimes family traditions don't change.

Big Henry Kane shouts over to Silver, "Don't forget, half eight Friday morning and as I said don't be late!"

Silver walks casually over to Henry and says to him that he thought he said he would lift him from the house. "Jesus you'll never change Paddy. I'll pick you up at your house at nine then. You're like a child. You need lifted and laid."

"And don't be bumping that horn, waking the whole street up," says Silver.

"I wonder would you give my head peace."

"I will see you on Friday and be up. We're not waiting. It's a long drive to the Puck." Silver is meandering around the market square and farmers are shaking hands with him and one farmer asks him to give him a hand loading some horses he bought. Silver walks the first horse up the ramp of the horsebox and the farmer follows up with the second horse and both are tied up. Silver goes down and takes the halter from a young lad who is holding the third horse but try as he might the horse will not go up the ramp. Silver gives the horse to the young fellow and tells him to just hold the halter loose as he and the farmer join hands and grip around the horse's rump and both heave but not a yard will the horse move.

Just at that Paddy Leaf Rooney appears and starts laughing. Leaf as he is called because he loves anything green, is revered as one of the most knowledgeable horse dealers in Belfast.

"Looks like he's not for moving. Does he stand you much?" Leaf asks the farmer. This is another way of asking how much he gave for the pony?

"I give twenty-two ten and ten bob back for luck." Again that means twenty-two pounds, ten shillings. Leaf takes the halter and of the young lad and hands it to young Docky who is his message boy and asks him to jog the pony up and down. He then takes a look at his teeth and declares that he's three year old. He then runs his hands down the pony's legs front and back. He grabs his tail and gives it a pull.

"Do you want to blow two pounds on him?" That means lose two pounds on the sale. The farmer laughs.

"I'll tell you what I'll do," he says, "give me twenty two pounds and its yours. He's not really the type of pony I want for the young girl but I'm not blowing two quid." Paddy Leaf asks him to hold out his hand and the big farmer holds out his giant hands and he slaps it and says you will take twenty pounds for him. After a bit of hand slapping the final slap on the hands and the deal is done. Leaf hands the farmer the money. Twenty pounds and ten shilling. Silver gets the luck penny of ten shillings. Leaf hands the pony to young Docky and tells him to walk him up to the yard and not to be throwing his leg over him but to walk him up to the yard easy.

Docky walks away with the pony and out of the Market Square and ties the halter Indian style around the pony's neck, throws his leg over it and sets sail for Milan Street stabling yard. He gets off it and his jeans are covered in dandruff and horsehair and just then Leaf walks in and just looks at him in disbelief.

"I suppose you got that on your jeans sitting in the barbers shop. Don't open your mouth. I should have known better. Anyway what does he go like?"

"He can trot for fun, Leaf, he's a real good goer."

"When he cools off, get him a bite of hay and a drink of water but wait till he cools off. He's boiling over the back. You probably galloped the whole way up here. You never give him a chance. I told you to walk him up."

* * *

It's coming up to nine o'clock on Friday and Big Kane pulls up outside Silver's house in the market and bumps his horn. Silver comes out with a wee grip and goes to the boot of the car, opens it and puts it in. Silver goes to get into the back but sees that the front seat is empty and he gets in beside Kane. After a few 'good mornings' and small talk, the car is speeding down the road. Hack starts the conversation and it is initially a bit of banter but then it becomes an inquisition.

"What was it like in jail Paddy?"

"Well it was no holiday camp that's for sure and the grub was terrible."

"Did you meet anyone you knew in there?"

"It would be easier to tell you who weren't in. It was full of guys form the Falls, the Market, Sandy Row, the Shankill and everywhere else in Belfast. A few countrymen were also in but they kept themselves to themselves and minded their own business and got on with it. Our crowd were slagging and shouting across the wings at night. It was like the London palladium some nights and I have to say there was a lot of funny people in there. But I just wanted to get on with my time, get it done and get to hell out of there."

Did you get a cell for yourself?" asks Joe?

"No I was doubled up as they call it with a guy from the Shankill. A good fellow called Sandy. He was the snout baron."

"What the hell is a snout baron when you're writing home?"

"He laid the horses and you punted in cigarettes or tobacco. It was a good old business. I stopped smoking while I was in and he didn't smoke so we swapped tobacco for fruit and chocolate. He was good to me and I had a bar of chocolate nearly every night."

"Here, we'll pull in and get a cup of tea. It's two hours to the Puck. I need a tightener – a good fry will do the trick," says Kane.

"That's fine by me," says Hack.

"And me too," says Joe.

"I couldn't look at a fry. A cup of tea will do me rightly," says Silver.

"Are you sick from the drink Paddy?"

"You could say that but I will be all right when I get a cure." The four men head in to a café and Silver tells the lads that's he is going for a walk.

"I told you, no drinking on this trip Paddy," says Kane.

"Look, I need one, just the one to settle me. My stomach is going mad and I'm waiting to throw up as you go around them bends like there's no tomorrow." Silver walks out and up the street into the nearest pub and walks in. "Give's a bottle of stout and a glass of whiskey and a wee glass of water along with that." The barman sets the drink up and within a few minutes a man introduces himself to Silver.

"I'm Sean Grace. I own a wee place down the road. I deal in the odd cow or two and I've met you at Allams sale yard. Aren't you Silver McKee?"

"That's me but I prefer being called Paddy."

"Sorry for that but that's the only name I've ever heard you being called. Weren't you mixed up in that Billy McCausland thing and went to jail.?"

"If I hear jail mentioned again this day I'll go mad. I'm a million miles away from Belfast and all I've been asked is, what was it like, did you know so and so. If that's all you want to talk about mister leave me a lone. I've about ten minutes, then I have to go."

"I want to tell you something I heard and I thought it might be useful to you. It's a story about Robinson and McCausland."

"And what's it got to do with me?"

"Well listen to the story I heard and you will know it could be..."

"As far away as the next lighthouse."

"But I heard on the grapevine that they used you and plotted against you to get rid of some counterfeit money. It was so McCausland would get the boy back and get rid of the dummy money."

"And what good would that do Robinson?"

"Well big McCausland bought the dummy money from him for about two bob in the pound and it was to fool the farmers and once they were paid and the child released, the job was done."

"I don't understand."

"Listen Paddy, they where in cahoots. The deeds of the house was a blinder. It was all a set up. They where trading with each other and trying to get away with out paying the farmers, then splitting the money."

"Jeepers, I've heard some tales in my time, but that beats banachar. I've heard it all today."

"Well you ask anyone in this town if I'm a man of my word and we'll leave it at that. I may take a drink too many at times but I'm a man of my word."

"Yes, just like myself. I think you're a dreamer," says Silver.

Sean calls the barman. "Give Paddy a drink and I'll have a large brandy. I just met the man from Belfast, Silver Mc Kee who as far as I know is the hardest street fighting man in the world."

Just then the door flies open and in walks Kane, Hack an Joe. "I'm only asking you once. Come now or we're going on."

Silver lifts his drink and lowers it in one go, puts the glass back on the bar counter and shakes hands with Sean. "As you see I must be on my way. My driver beckons." Silver burst out laughing as he follows the three men as they walk down to the car. As the car drives off a bit of an argument between Kane and Silver arises and Kane tells him that he promised there'd be no drinking on the trip. After a few heated minutes Silver apologises and says that he will not have another drink on the journey. Kane tells him that he's not worried about him drinking but the fact that him Hack and Joe don't drink. Could he not be dry at least for the journey as the car now stank like a brewery. About half an hour later Hack and Joe fall fast asleep in the back seat when Silver asks Kane for his opinion on the story that he'd been told in the pub.

"In my opinion, I've never heard such a yarn but I could believe anything that involves Harry and Billy. They're two gangsters." Later they arrive outside their hotel and the four men get their cases and walk into the lobby, which is packed with men women and children running mad about the place. Big Kane walks over to the lobby desk followed by the other three and in a few minutes they have signed in. A porter leads them to their room and Silver finishes up sharing with Hack. Joe and Kane share the other room. The men agree to meet in the lobby in an hour and then they will make there way to the fair. Silver and Hack both change their clothes and have a wash and shave and head down to the lobby and have a seat as they wait on Joe and Kane. It seems like everyone from Belfast is here, as people walk over to Hack and Silver and exchange pleasantries. Joe and Kane now appear and the four men leave and head for the fair.

* * *

As they enter the square they see King Puck hoisted in a cage above everyone's head. The fair is now officially opened and the dealing has begun. Horses are being trotted up and down the street as prospective customers cast their eyes over them.

"How many have you orders for Henry?" asks Silver?

"Sixty. Forty, horses for Scotland, twenty for England and twenty donkeys for Blackpool for the kiddies rides on the beach."

"You have a full order book then?"

"Joe will probably buy the odd one or two and that will do us." Just then an appaloosa is being trotted by Kane on the long rein and he asked the man trotting him, "is he broke for riding?" Kane looks around him and sees young Fra Ward and Jim Haughey and calls them over. "One of you throw your leg over that cob and see what he's like." Fra Ward steppes forward and gets a leg up, and trots off up and down the street. "How much is he?" asks Kane.

"He's sixty quid, Sir and not a penny less sir. I'll take him home before I take a penny less."

"Well you may be taking him home then." Kane tells Fra to jump off him and he says to the seller, "I'll tell you what I'll do. I will give you forty quid for him."

"No chance Sir. He's sixty pounds and that is what I need for him." Kane turns his back and walks up the fair.

"He'll be back before it's all over," he says to Hack. Joe tells Kane there's a thousand horses at the fair and its early days. Kane mingles among the horses followed now by a growing entourage of Joe, Hack, Fra, and Jim. Silver has disappeared. After some time Kane has bought twenty horses of all shapes and sizes and five donkeys. He decides it's time for something to eat and he takes Fra, Jim and Hack and Joe for a feed in the hotel. As Jim and Fra have been helping him all day, this is their reward for their help. The young guys would do it for nothing, as they love horses and anything to do with them. As the group is eating the conversation turns to Fra and Jim.

"That was some job your Da done on that yard of mine in Panton Street. There must he twenty thousand bricks in it."

"Yes. my Da's a master bricklayer but I'm not going to be a bricky. I'm going to go on the boats and see the world. What about you, young Ward?"

"As soon as I get back, I'm going to sea school unless I can get away quicker. I have been down at the pool a few times and a man called Jackie Ross has told me one of the days I go down, I might get a pier head jump."

"What the hell's a pier head jump?" Hack and Joe burst out laughing thinking it's a double entendre but Fra goes on to explain that maybe a wee coaster comes in and at the last minute they need a galley boy or a deck boy and it's all a matter of being there at the right time. "So I will see what happens when I get back. I'm going to Southampton." "You're a cert to get a boat there," says Jim.

Just as the team is finishing off the meal, in walks Silver and draws up a chair and sits down.

"Want something to eat, Paddy?" asks Kane.

"No. I had something earlier on. Who's these two young lads here?"

"That's two of Joe's jockeys, young Ward and Haughey. They thumbed it the whole way down here but I think we can squeeze them in going home. They will be helping me and Joe with whatever animals we buy."

"Are you a Ward from Osman Street? I knew your older brother Jimmy. It was terrible what happened to him in Birmingham?"

Fra asks, "Are you really Silver McKee? Big Henry was telling us about you and how you knocked out a cow with one dig in the markets."

"Well, I don't know if I knocked the cow out or not but it didn't get up for a while." Silver laughs.

"I'm going to be like you one day," says Fra, "the hardest man in Belfast."

"Listen son. I don't know where you get your ideas but its no cakewalk being called a hard man. You never get peace because there's always some young buck waiting to take you on, especially when they are drunk. So take my advice and get a good job, a few quid and forget the hard man thing. Street fighting is for mugs."

"Well lets change the subject,"says Kane. "What were you doing all day? Didn't see much of you about Paddy."

"I met a few Market men, the Murdochs and we had a couple of bottles of stout and a bit of craic."

"Did they buy any animals?" asks Joe.

"They bought the loveliest appaloosa you ever set eyes on. I think it was Lawrence bought it and he said there's not another like it in Ireland."

"Told you! You should have pushed your man and bought the horse" says Hack.

"It may not be the same horse," says Kane.

"Oh, it's the same horse all right!" The man gave it one trot down the street, told Lawrence Murdoch that some Belfast lad had ridden it for you and that was it. "The deal done."

"That's the one I was riding," says Fra excitedly to his mate Jim. " I told you he was some horse. I'd have bought him myself if I had the money and rode him home."

"Do you know how long that would take son?" says Silver..."about as long as it will take you to be a hard man. Forget about all that. Get a job when you go home and stop dreaming." Fra stands up and although he is young, he would face Goliath and is fit as a fiddle and can fight but he's not a match for Silver, not now anyway. Joe tells Fra to sit down and to mind his manners when he's with adults and to act like a gentleman. Fra apologises and sits down.

"Look, there's a sing song across the road in the pub and it will be a bit of craic. I know youse men aren't drinking but you can have an orange along with the lads." Henry calls for the bill and pays for the meals and they all get up and walk out and over to the pub. As they get their seats, its like the whole of Belfast are there: Lazy Tom Clarke, Vinty Hamilton, Joe McLaren and some men from the Market area. The band is playing and the master of ceremonies decides its time to call some singers. Silver is called for a song and duly obliges to the raptures of the crowd and then Jim Haughey gets up and sings a song and he gets an even better applause. The next to sing is a woman from Buttevant, a local town and she is as good as a professional and goes down a storm.

"That's the best singer tonight," calls the master of ceremonies. He then asks her to sing two more songs. The crowd are loving it. Then the master of ceremonies says, "We now have a young man from Belfast called Fra Ward who I'm told is going to appear on Opportunity Knocks but we got him first. A round of applause for the young man from Belfast. He's a great singer!" Fra gets up after a bit of persuasion and is handed the mike and that's the last time that the master of ceremonies will get the mike back. Fra pulls the house down and they wont let him get off the stage. He sings song after song and to make it better, they pass the hat around for him and hand him about twenty pounds after he finishes. People are up back slapping the newly found star and he gets carried out of the bar on the shoulders of Lazy Tom, Big Vinty and the rest of the Belfast crowd.

After a few more days in at the Puck, it's now time to head home. Kane and

Joe have arranged transport for the horses and donkeys and are loading up the car when Fra and Jim appear.

"I thought youse where travelling with the horses," Big Kane says.

"Can we get a lift home in the car? The lorry driver wants us to travel in the back of the lorry along with the horses." After a few minutes of haggling they all pile into the car. Three in the front and three in the back and they head off up the road for home. As they travel up the road the conversation turns to Silver's drinking and how if he didn't drink, he'd not get into as much bother. Kane is a reformed drinker as is Hack but Joe never touched it and Fra and Jim have just started drinking. Kane explains that's since he stopped drinking three years previous, his life had turned around and he only wished he'd stopped early in his life or in fact had never touched the stuff. Joe interrupts to tell them that as he never drank and it's all double Dutch to him and he's going to go asleep.

"I'm knackered as well, so I'm going to sleep," Hack says and asks for a bit of quiet. Youse don't have to shout as there's nobody deaf in the car. Silver explains that if they had the misfortune in life he had, they all would be drinking. Kane tell him that there is no such thing as a lost cause and if he tried to go off it, things might change. Silver informs Kane that he sounds like a preacher and he was also going to have a sleep. The car goes quiet and in a few hours they arrive outside Silver's house in the market.

"Let me get my case and thanks for the few days away. It was great. I will come up some day during the week to see you all. When are the horses due to arrive anyway?"

"Some time tonight, or about eleven o'clock on Monday morning. Depends how long they are held at the border."

"Here, one of youse young lads come down for me; I will come up and help you get them ready for the boat, Kane."

Fra pipes up right away. "I will come down for you. Jim and me will dander down and let you know."

"Good lads." Silver goes to the boot and lifts out his case then shouts in the window, "You're a great singer son. I'd stick to that, never mind your other ideas."

"Good luck !"He shouts very loudly to waken Hack and Joe and as they look around themselves they say in unison, "Belfast already!"

* * *

A day later Joe's yard is over run with horses and donkeys and even a mare has foaled as soon as she landed in the yard. Silver walks through the wicket gate along with Fra and Jim. Both lads love it, they are with their idol. They are in the company of Silver and it's like a status symbol when you live in a district where hard men and hard drinkers are held in so high esteem and Silver is both. Just then another man arrives. He's an old friend of Silver and Joe. His name is Stumpy Joe Hamill and his specialty is plaiting a horses mane and tail and tiding up any blemishes on a horse. The next person to arrive is Josie Riley and he's no sooner into the yard when Joe calls him.

"Go around to Joe Mc Caulfield's chemist and get me a wee packet of potash and don't be long." Josie takes the money and runs around to the chemist shop and within minutes he is back and hands the potash to Joe. Young Josie is the next generation below Fra Ward and Jim Haughey and when they leave school and start work he will hopefully become the main jockey for Joe and that's the way it has been for generations.

On up the yard Yacko is paring a donkey's hoof and Stumpy is plaiting straw into a big horses mane. Then comes the tricky part of blowing their eyes up and it's a bit like removing bags under a humans eyes but in this case above a horses eyes. A pin is first pierced into the hollow above the horse's eye and then a piece of hay is placed in the small hole; a painless operation but tricky. Stumpy then blows down the piece of hay and blows and puffs and just like magic the dinge or bags disappear. He then gets the potash and mixes some in some water and takes a small dabbing brush made out of horse hair not unlike a mans wobbling brush and begins to work his magic. Then the grey hairs around the horse eyes are dabbed and the hair turns a light reddish colour. The magic of potash begins to work. Some people would ask why are they doing that to the poor horse. But all in all, it's painless and it made the horse look better and most of all it fools the vet who checks all horses going on the boat. Although he's a vet he worked for the council and couldn't age a horse by its teeth so he went on looks and as long as the horses weren't lame and could jog up and down he was quite happy to let them board the boat for Glasgow. Stumpy could take an old nag and turn it into a thoroughbred in looks at least. Silver is helping Joe wash a few horses when Big Kane comes up the yard and looks around him.

"Will they all be ready for half seven, Joe"

"Hello Stumpy!" cries Kane and Stumpy walks over and shakes hands with him. Joe tells Kane that they will be leaving the yard at six o'clock and they where going straight down the Falls Road and down by the Big Clock to the

Glasgow boat. It would take a half an hour or forty-five minutes. "Did McKee come up?" asks Kane.

Silver comes out of a stable and shouts, "Yes McKee came up and if you got your coat off, we would get this lot done quicker."

Yacko shouts, "Aye! and if it snowed in July we could throw snowballs!"

Joe shouts at Yacko and tells him to get on with what he's doing and to mind his own business. Joe calls Fra Ward and tells him to go and get a few of the lads and bring them around after six o'clock, as he would need all the hands he can get. Kane walks out of the yard to his car and walks in again with a large hessian bag. He tips it up on a cart sitting in the yard.

"There's a load of new halters. Make sure every horse has one on. Don't worry about the donkeys, they'll be all right. They'll walk behind the horses."

About an hour later all the horses are haltered and tied in fours and the donkeys are mingling about the yard. Every one is ready for the ride down the Falls Road to the docks where they will be loaded on the Royal Ulsterman of the Burns and Laird line. Silver puts on his Crombie and grabs his ash plant as he is leading the procession.

"Okay! Everybody ready?" and everyone shouts "YES!"

Half of the Falls Road is there: Vinty Boyle, Go Go Riley, Charley Ward, Peter and Tony Clarke, John Manning, Anthony and Gerard Hughes, Joe's two nephews, Joe Councillor Connolly and Geordie Scott as well as Fra Ward. He is riding the lead horse with three tied beside him, followed by Jim Haughey and then Josie Riley and Geordie Adams. Fred Plumbo, Peter Clarke and the two Tohills follow and Jim O'Riley is taking up the rear on a grey mare. Yacho has been assigned to herd the donkeys behind the horses along with Geordie Scott. The two main gates are open and Silver leads the parade out of the yard. A few of the horses are shying but after a few streets they have settled down.

The horses are going to Glasgow to a man called Alec White who has been a customer of Joe and Big Kane for years. As the horses and donkeys move off up Albert Street unto the Falls road, Silver stops as a trolley bus goes by. Then he waves everyone onto the main road.

Unexpectedly another trolley bus comes down the road and the sparks start to explode from the over head lines and one of the horse ridden by Vinty Boyle rears up. Stumpy Joe who is walking behind grabs it by the head and settles it down and the trolley bus disappears off down the road.

Fra Ward who is leading the herd says to Jim who is along side him, "Isn't this the greatest feeling. It's like being the King of the Falls and being with Silver what more is there in life?"

As the horses are lead down the cobbled road at the dockside, the vet starts inspecting them but in truth he is over whelmed by the numbers and waves everyone on into the sheds where the dock workers take over and load the horses into the hold of the ship through the gun port doors. After all the animals are loaded big Kane tells every one that he will meet them in Victor's Ice Cream shop in Divis Street and he will treat them all to a smokie. So as he, Joe, Stumpy, and Silver get in the car and drive off, all the lads are walking up to the ice cream shop where true to his word big Kane and the others are already seated. Every one of the boys got their smokie and some that weren't even down at the docks got one. This is the biggest shipment of horses big Kane had made since he went into the horse trade and it wouldn't be the last.

Unnoticed to most of us, a real Belfast character Big Josie Walsh had been following the parade and he loved big Henry who was quite good to him. Josie was a bit mentally challenged and he could eat ice cream for fun.

"I never saw anyone drink a smokie so fast as big Josie!" says Joe Hughes. as Big Josie swallowed the smokie. After everyone was finished Big Kane handed all the riders or jockeys a half crown each, not caring that most of them had done nothing. A few minutes later Silver asks Kane would he run him home and Kane duly obliges as Joe only lived up the street and Stumpy who was from Portadown was staying in his house. As Kane and Silver are in the car alone Silver asks him how did he manage to get off that drink?

Kane replied, "With a great deal of difficulty. In the end I went to Alcoholics Anonymous and I suppose it all started there."

"Now can I ask you another question, as a friend?"

"Fire away." says Kane. "If I can answer it I will tell you."

"Do you think Harry and Billy plotted against me?"

Kane takes a long pause and looks Silver straight in the face. "Do you think they did?" "If I thought they done that on me I'd kill both of them with my bare hands." "Which one stood to benefit the most out of the shuffle?" Kane asks.

"That's the part that confuses me."

"First things first," says Kane. "Whose money was it because nobody seems to know if it was McCausland or Robinsons or the farmers?"

"Look between me and you, I was the delivery boy and I was getting a hundred quid for doing the job but as soon as I sat down to do the change over for wee John, the cops piled in and the whole thing went pear shaped."

"Who had the money then?"

"I had it but I didn't get a chance to do anything with it. Then wee John ran into the lounge where we were sitting and I was arrested along with big Sam.

The money was confiscated and it was made a ward of court or something. The judge keeps putting the case back and I think it's starting to smell. There's something not right here. Billy put up the deeds of his house for the loan of the money and I think Harry wanted his house, so it was better for him if it all went wrong."

"How much did he borrow off Harry?"

"Ten grand against a house worth fifteen or twenty thousand."

"Was he mad?"

"He needed the money badly and Harry told him in the Grand Central Hotel, he'd lend it to him on them terms."

"Look Paddy. I'm going to drive you home. This car is freezing with no heater running but I'm as wise as ever. I don't know who is the devil in this."

"Anyway thanks for bailing me out. I appreciate it."

"So you know I'm always there for you, if you need me."

"Fair plays, good sport." Silver walks towards his house opens the door and Kane drives off. The car is no sooner out of the street than Silver pops his head out, looks up and down the street and walks out, pulling the hall door behind him.

Chapter 9

Give me a glass of whiskey and a bottle of stout," says Silver, as he stands at the bar in a packed Mandeville club. A sing song is going on and it's rather subdued as a singer belts out his song. Silver lowers the whiskey into himself.

"You must have needed that Paddy," quips the barman.

"So would you, if you had been where I was."

"Where was that then?"

"I was a way to the Puck Fair for three days and not one of the men I was with took a drink. In fact all they done was preach about John Barleycorn whoever he is? Set me up another drink.

That singer's putting my head away."

"He's not a bad chanter, Paddy."

"There was a kid came home with us from the Puck and he's the best singer I've heard in years. He's from up the Falls and his mate wasn't too bad either."

"What did you call him?"

"Fra Ward. He could belt the songs out like Mario Lanza?"

"I know him he comes in here some Sunday nights but he's a bit on the young side. He shouldn't really be served any drink, but he does no one any harm and as long as he doesn't lift his hands it's okay. I have never heard him singing but I saw him go to town. He can fight for fun. It was outside the Plaza one night and he can hit like a hammer. He wouldn't be in your league, Paddy, you know what I mean, but he's a hard man among his own mates and is gaining a bit of a name for himself."

"I will have to keep on my toes then – a young pretender. Seemed a nice kid. I knew his elder brother, Jimmy. He was killed in a fight in Birmingham. A smashing fellow – was only about twenty-eight when he died. It was a terrible tragedy and his mother never got over it. They never do, it stays with them all their lives and they just get on with life but they suffer in silence. Here give me a halfun and another bottle of stout." As the night goes on Silver asks the barman to call him a taxi from Silver cabs.

"Is that the only firm you use, Paddy?"

"Yes, it's the one I remember best." Both Silver and the barman laugh. "The other firms keep you waiting all night but Silver cabs will be here in five minutes. You can bet on it." Just like clockwork, a guy comes through the door shouting, "Taxi for McKee."

Silver is finishing his drink and shouts, "Two minutes... wait till I get to the toilet. I'll be out in a minute."

Silver goes to the toilet and makes his way out of the Mandeville Club and gets in the taxi.

"Where to?" asks the driver.

"Do you know Castlereagh well?"

"To be honest Mister, no but I will find it, if you give me directions."

"Okay. Well, head for the Castlereagh Road and I will give directions to where I'm going." "Do you live up there mister?" asks the driver.

"No but my wife does." The driver scratches his head and ponders what's going on. "To tell you the truth son, the wife left me, took the baby girl with her and went back to her mothers."

"They're all like that. My wife done the same but she was back in a week and glad to get back," the driver says boldly.

"My wife must be a whole lot different. She's been gone over a month now. I thought she would be back in a day or two. So I'm going up to her ma's to bring her and the baby home, if she will come."

"Hope there's not going to be any trouble mister, any cops or anything like that."

"There will be no trouble. You just drive the car and be quiet because it seems every car I get into, its an inquisition or someone preaching about the devils drink and John Barleycorn."

"That's a book mister. I read it; by a fellow called Jack London. Reminds me of the stories I hear about Silver McKee. You don't know if they're true or not. You know what Belfast is like. We tend to exaggerate."

"Tell me one of them stories. I'd love to hear it and who is this Silver fellow?"

"I never met him but I heard my da talking about him knocking a bull out. Some say it was a wee calf." Silver laughs. "Then there was the one where he fought Stormy Weatherall up the Shankill Road. One of our drivers took him up and him and Stormy had a fair go but all the oul dolls beat him with brushes and shovels and anything they could get their hands on. Another one of our drivers had to rescue him and Stormy and get them off the Shankill before the two of them where killed."

"He must be some pup that Silver fellow. Have you ever met him yourself son? No he lives in the Market district but we never get calls from down there and I live on the Antrim Road. So the chances of running in to him are slim. I would love to meet him."

"Some day you might run into him."

"They say he's about six feet tall and as broad as he is tall."

Silver laughs, "That is some description. He must be a giant of a man. Here turn up this lane. Drive to the top and pull up beside the house. I'm going in for a minute or so but I won't be long. I'm not for staying." The car stops outside a large country house, which is in complete darkness, and Silver gets out and knocks on the door. After a few minutes the lights go on and the front door opens. It is Mary's mother.

"What do you think you're doing, rapping good people out of their bed and you as drunk as a skunk?"

"I'm here to ask my wife to come home with our child, if you don't mind?

"Could you not have come at a reasonable hour, without being full as a lord and wakening everyone up including your child that you haven't seen in months?"

Just then Mary comes to the door and is crying as Silver tries to get her to come home. "I miss you and the child and I've a taxi ready to take you home now."

Mary looks at Silver and tells him,"Paddy while you're taking drink I'm staying with my mum and if you don't stop drinking, I will be seeing a solicitor."

"Now what would you be doing, going to see a solicitor about? Sure I never laid a hand on you."

"I can assure you if you ever laid a hand on me it would be your first and last time and if you want to really know why I will go and see a solicitor. For a divorce,."

Silver laughs, "Our religion doesn't do divorce." He is laughing as if it's a joke.

Mary replies, "But ours does. Now would you take yourself and that taxi away from this door before I call the police and I'm not joking," says Mary's mother. After some arguing and some haggling like they where horse-trading Silver turns and walks away from the door and gets into the taxi.

"No luck mister? Where to now?

"Take me to the nearest pub. I need a drink."

"It's Sunday night mister. You haven't a snowballs chance in hell of getting a drink, especially at this time of the night. It's five past eleven."

"Well then take me home."

"Where's home mister?"

"That wee place they call the Market, where I was born and bred and used to work."

"You must know Silver, Mister. That's where he's from and they say everyone in the markets know him. Is that true?"

"Well, firstly it's called the Market, the place where they buy cattle, horses and sheep is the markets. Not where the people live – that's the real Market."

"Jesus mister, don't be eating the face of me. I only heard of it being called the markets never anything else."

"Well, now you know the difference. You won't make the same mistake twice." "Okay. Where in the Market ? What street?".

"Just stop here. There's a friend of mine I want to see." As Silver is getting out the car the driver says, "that's will be twenty-five bob."

Silver gets out and is fumbling with some money and he shouts down the street: "Stack!

What did you call that man who wanted a word with me?"

Stack walks down to the taxi and says, "Hello. Do you have to shout your business all over the street at this hour of night Silver?"

The taxi driver looks at him and asks, "Are you the real Silver McKee?"

"Some day's son, I wish I'd never heard the name but as sure as the priest said mass on the altar, I'm your man."

"A pound will do Silver. I'm only too glad to meet you. Wait till I tell my da I had you in the taxi." Silver hands the driver some money and is searching for more money and the taxi driver says that's enough and drives off.

"Now what are you on about?"

"Stack, what's your mans name whose looking me."

"He's a big English man and he's thinking of opening a scrap yard in Eliza Street but let me correct that. He's a rubber dealer."

"What does he want from me?"

"Me and him have been dealing about for a while and he knows that nothing moves without your say so. He's worried about local opposition from the likes of Barney Ross and your other big friend Kane, although he's up the Falls, but all he wants is to know the score."

"Well he's no worry with Kane and sure Barney has his own hawkers so what's the problem?"

"I'll tell you the problem. He's a cockney and an ex-army officer and he's trying to get a business off the ground. How would you feel trying to start a business in the east end of London?"

"I follow what you mean Stack. Call and see me over in Allams in the morning and we'll arrange a meet. By the way what has you out tonight at this time, Stack?"

"I lost my wee dog and I've been searching all night for him. The child is crying her eyes out; I can't go home without him."

Silver points across the road. "Is that him?"

"Fuck me! I'm out all night looking for him and you're half drunk and you find him. Mick, come here Mick!" cries Stack. The wee dog wags its tail and walks over to the two men. Stack lifts the dog, bids Silver good night, and as he's walking away he shouts.

"I'll see you in the morning. I'm away home and I'll maybe get a bit of sleep." Silver walks down the street and puts the key in the door and walks into his house. As usual he plants himself down on a chair and remains there till morning fast asleep.

Next morning Silver is awakened by the door being knocked loudly and he gathers himself up and goes to the curtain and has a look out. It's Stack and another man who doesn't know or recognise and he's unsure whether to open the front door. Again the door is being knocked and he can hear Stack calling his name. Silver opens the door and Stack tells him that he looks like death warmed up and introduces him to John Walsh. Silver invites both men in and tells them to take a seat while he makes a cup of tea.

As Silver is in the scullery making tea, John says to Stack, "For fucks sake mate, that mans not capable of looking after himself and you're asking me to send him to London to sort out my problem there?"

"You'll see a different man when he gets a cup of tea into him."

"Do you not mean a cup of whiskey? That mans dying on his feet." Silver walks into the living room and sets down two cups of tea in front of Walsh and Stack. He then walks back and gets himself a cup and sits down in his usual seat that he now literally lives in.

"What's the story then? How can I help you sir?"

"Well I don't know if you're the right man for the job. I was expecting something completely different but Stack assures me you're the man for the job."

"So what do you want me to do? Run it by me and I will tell you if I want the job or not."

"I used to own a little scrap yard in the east end of London and redevelopment came along. So these two brothers came to me and offered me what seemed a fortune for the place and I agreed. It's a messy deal, forty grand up front and three payments of ten grand making a total of seventy grand?"

"So what happened, but before you say anything I can probably guess."

"I got the forty and another five and then that was it. They refused to pay the other twenty five and the yard now has a multi-storey car park where it stood."

"What's a multistory car park when you're writing home mister?"

"London, unlike Belfast has far too many cars and when the people drive into the city they need somewhere to park their cars and that's what's standing on my yard and I got done out of twenty five thousand."

"So you want me to go to London to collect the outstanding debt."

"Yes, that's the general story and if you get it I will give you twenty-five hundred quid."

"That's a lot of money. So who are these brothers?"

"The Richardsons. They are also scrap dealers but rough men and as the money was coming under the counter I haven't a leg to stand on. What do you mean coming under the counter. Well, so as to avoid tax on it, the deal, forty grand is declared and you pay the tax and the rest is given in cash. It's a regular thing in the property business."

"Anything's better than the taxman getting it," says Silver. "What time of the morning is it?" John looks at his watch and tells Silver it is eleven o'clock.

"Jesus, I was to be at Allam's at nine o'clock. I suppose that's the end of that job. So how do I get to London and how do I find these guys?"

"I will give you the fare for the boat and a few quid to keep you going and an address for the Richardson's. They won't be hard to find. They have a scrap yard in the East End and are pretty well known."

* * *

A few days later Silver is packing his case and Stack is standing beside him and is telling him that this is his chance to get in trade for himself. If he gets the money for Walsh, he could buy a house and buy and sell cattle.

"Why what's wrong with this house?"

Stack looks around him and says; "Well it's no mansion now, is it?"

"It will do me my day. I was born here and hopefully it's where I'll die."

"Okay, come on. You'll have to catch the boat. It sails at eight o'clock". Silver hands Stack the key of the house and tells him to try and get someone to tidy it up.

"...and theres a pound note you can give them but get someone I know. I don't want strangers running in and out of here." Stack and Silver arrive at the docks and Silver boards the Heysham boat after bidding Stack his farewells.

Silver is sitting in the lounge on the Heysham Boat when one of the waiters walks over to him and sits beside him. It's young Fra Ward; he's got a job on the Heysham Boat. "Where you going Silver?"

"I'm going to London on a bit of business and I can see you got yourself on the boats just as you said you would."

"Have you a cabin Silver?"

"No. I didn't bother. Sure it's not a long journey."

"Sit tight here. I'll go and see what I can do." A few minutes later Fra returns and tells Silver to leave his drink and follow him. Fra leads him down to a cabin and Silver asks how much it is for the night.

"Nothing," replies Fra. "I was telling the chief steward whose from our road and he said you can have it buck shee. Throw your case there and I'll bring you back up to the lounge. When you're ready for a kip I'll not be far a way. Give me a shout and I'll bring you down here again." About an hour or so later Silver calls Fra and asks him to bring him down to the cabin because he would never find it in a month of Sundays. Fra walks him down through some alleyways opens the cabin door and helps him in, as by now he's half drunk.

"Some day I want to be like you Silver and I will."

"I told you before son. Do what your doing. Forget about that hard man thing. It's all an illusion and a life of madness."

The next morning the boat pulls into Heysham and is tying up. Silver is awakened as Fra walks into the cabin and rouses him. "Right Silver! Time to get out of here, unless you want to pay. Just get yourself ready and I will get you a cup of tea but be sharpish. The passengers will be disembarking soon."

"What do you mean, disembarking?"

"I only found out when I joined the boat, it means getting off. So give your face a rub and I will be right back with a cup of tea. You take sugar and milk?"

"Plenty of sugar son. I need something to sweeten my stomach." After a few minutes Fra returns with a cup of tea and Silver is dressed and ready to go.

"Get that into you and I will walk you up to the gangway." Silver drinks the tea and rubs his hands, grabs his case and follows Fra up through the alleyways and up to the gangway. Fra sticks his hand out and shakes hands with Silver and wishes him good luck.

Silver says to Fra, "I wont forget this son and I want to hear you sing again. So I will meet you when I come back home."

"No problem Silver."

As Silver is walking down the gangway he meets an old friend from the Market called Harry Watson and they just happen to be travelling on the same train up to London. As they sit on the train Harry tells Silver that's he's going for a boat in Southampton and if he went with him he could get him a job on the boats.

"I wish I could Harry but I've a bit of business to do in London and when I get that done I'm home again. England's not for me. Belfast is enough."

"Where you going to stay in London Paddy?"

"Some bed and breakfast I think."

"Look I will give you an address to go to. It's a wee woman from Carrickhill who owns a lodging house. I used to stay with her and she's handy paid, and a great grubber."

"What's the address?"

"I will write it down for you..." Harry pulls out a Woodbine packet and a pencil and writes down the street name... "Woodstock Grove in Shepherds Bush. There's a pub at the corner called the Stagecoach. Walk down Richmond Street and halfway down, it goes into a vee and it's the third door. Tell her I sent you and you will have no problem. There's a lot of the Belfast men stay with there, and she makes grub just like you get at home. It's like home from home."

"You seem to know London very well Harry. Did you ever hear the name Richardson Brothers mentioned among the Belfast lads?"

"No but I think I know who you mean."

"So what's their story?"

"Bad news Silver. Weapons men. There's them and the Krays, another two brothers and they literally run London. Can I ask what your business is Silver because I may be able to put you in touch with some body who could put you wide."

"To be honest I don't know what the hell I'm doing here but I will give it a try. They owe a friend of mine a few quid. I'm over to collect it."

"You will have to go team handed and I can tell you, you've two hopes; Bob Hope and no hope. They run London. It's not Belfast. I'll give you a name and you contact this guy and he may get you what you need - a few lads and a heater."

"A heater? Your making it sound like a gangster film. I'm only going to collect a few grand."

"Let me tell you, you go and see Spotter Hanna. He lives off the Edgeware Road but you will get him in a club called the Stage and Radio most days. Tell him who you are. He probably knows of you and tell him you're a friend of mine but it's not going to be a tea party. You're moving into the big league Silver and I mean the big league. These men are real gangsters." An announcement comes on the public address:

CHANGE AT CREWE FOR EUSTON STATION

"Right, this is where we get off and if you really want to know how I feel about this job you're on, I'd get on the next boat home."

"Look Harry, you know me well enough. I never went team handed in my life. I always done everything on my own."

"I know Paddy, but this is a different ball game. These guys would shoot you for a dollar." As they both get off the train and board another train for London, they get lucky and get an empty carriage.

"Can you get a drink on these trains Harry?"

"As soon as it starts moving the bar will be opened and you'll get a drink but it's expensive. You're heading for London now and nothings cheap." Silver hands the cigarette package to Harry and tells him to write down that man Spotters name. Harry writes it down and the name of the club. "He's a sound man from up the Falls Road. He's well known around London and has all the connections and knows everybody. Before you do a thing at least talk to him, I promise you, you'll need him."

After having a few drinks and a bit of yarning the train pulls in to Houston station and the two men alight from the train.

"Well this is where we part company, Paddy. I wish you luck. You're going to need it."

"Listen Harry. Would you not stay with me for a few days and put me right. I've never been in this place before and I'll tell you this. When I'm finished what I have to do, I'll be back home like a rocket."

"Tell you what. I don't have to join the boat until Thursday, so I can give you a day of my time."

"What's the boat your joining Harry?"

"The Mary, Paddy."

"The Mary! That's the name of my wife."

"The Queen Mary, Paddy, the biggest liner in the world."

"Brilliant Harry! Lets go, one day won't make much difference. I won't forget you doing me this turn, Harry thanks! Let's get a taxi."

Both men get into a taxi and Harry tells the driver to take them to 3 Woodstock Grove. "You know Paddy. If you stay here any length of time you'll have to learn to use the tubes."

"No, no, not for me them trains that run under the ground."

"It's a brilliant system once you get to know the score. You won't want to travel any other way, and when you pay this fare, you will know what I mean." The taxi pulls up outside Mary Annes in Woodstock Grove and Silver asks the driver for the price of the fare.

"That will be two pounds, ten shilling sir."

Silver looks at him. "We've only travelled around about a mile and you want fifty bob."

The driver points to the clock. "I don't make the price sir, that does." Silver pays up and the driver takes off and stops a bit down the street and shouts, "You'd be as well listening to your mate and get the tubes. They'd suit you rightly."

Silver shouts after him to come back and say that. Harry tells Silver to take it easy. The landlady wouldn't like any trouble around her house. Silver and Harry walk in and Harry talks to Mary Anne and tells her Silver is a friend of his and he needs somewhere to stay for a few weeks.

"Another one over to see the time. I don't know why they bother coming the whole way over here to London and within a week or two they're away back home but anyway I have a room that will suit him. Mary shows Silver up to his room and tells him its three pounds a week and I don't want any bother so if your quiet you'll be all right. Young Gerry Conway just went home last night.

He's over here, back and forward like a YoYo. I don't know how he can be annoyed."

"This will do fine missus. Do you want paid now?"

"Well that makes a change. Yes, it's three pounds a week and you get a bit of breakfast in the morning and a good dinner at night. Its cabbage, ribs and spuds, tonight and I serve it between five and seven o'clock - no later. Silver opens his case and takes his belongings out and puts his suit on a hanger and his other clothes into an old set of drawers.

Harry shouts up the stairs, "Are you ready Paddy?"

"I'll be down in a few minutes. I'm just putting my clothes away."

* * *

Harry and Silver are sitting in the Stage and Radio club having a drink when in walks Spotter. Harry gets up and asks Spotter to join them and Spotter sits down in the company. Harry orders a drink and introduces Spotter to Silver.

"I know all about you. My mates brother works with you in Belfast, Croaky McNally."

"Small world," says Silver."Which one is it? Tommy? He's away a few years now, wouldn't know him if I seen him."

"He hasn't changed much. He's working today anyway. What has you in London?"

"I'm over on a bit of business and I met Harry coming off the boat."

"You will always meet someone on the Heysham Boat. There's always somebody crossing over for some reason or another. Some come over drunk, sober up and they're away home again. Then there's the guy running away from a bad marriage but I never knew any of our type to be over on business unless it's not on the up and up."

"Tell Spotter what you're over for. He's sound. You can tell him anything," says Harry.

Silver starts to explain to Spotter and half way through the conversation Spotter interrupts. "Do you know who you're dealing with, Silver? This isn't Belfast. These people are real gangsters and they won't pay up easily and they are always team handed and weapons men. Even fire the odd shot if you know what I mean. Do you want my advice. Stay around a week or so and go home and tell big whatever his name is you tried but there's no chance they'll pay."

"I couldn't do that; I'm getting a couple of grand if I get the money and I could be doing with a few quid." After a few more drinks, Harry says that he is heading off down to the Hamp (the name seamen call Southampton) and he wishes Silver well and tells Spotter to look after him. "It's his first time in the Big Smoke." Harry leaves and Silver and Spotter get deep in conversation and the more they drink the braver they become and the Richardson's seem less of a threat. Both men get drunk and Spotter tells him he can stay in his house but Silver declines and tells him he's staying in a place called Mary Anne's.

"Yes I know her. I stayed there when I first came over here. I will get you over there and I will meet you tomorrow and we can discuss what way best to go about this job. But let me tell you. We will need a team. It's not a solo run, I guarantee you that." Both men leave and get a taxi over to Shepherd's Bush.

"Here we are driver, stop here. I'm not going in Silver, as she will keep me all night talking, but I will be here at nine o'clock in the morning."

"Just one thing Spotter, I'd rather you called me Paddy, please."

"Well I'm all right with Spotter. My big mate Tucker and me will be there in the morning. Good night and good luck Paddy." Silver walks off into the house and makes his way up to his room, throws himself down on the bed and falls asleep.

Next morning as arranged Spotter is sitting along with big Tucker in Mary Anne's living room as Mary calls Silver to get up. "There's people looking for you." Silver comes down the stairs and looks at Spotter and Tucker who are dressed like tailors dummies.

"Morning Spotter. I suppose this is your friend Tucker. Where are you pair going, to court?"

"We're going to have a look at the Richardsons, that's what, and you better get changed into your best. We don't want to look like nobodies when we go across the water. I thought we where across the water. Both men laugh. "Go up and get changed and try and look your best. These guys need to see they're dealing with serious people, not idiots." Silver goes back upstairs and returns about ten minutes later dressed to the nines.

"Not too bad now. You look the part. Now when we go over to The Craven Arms we will just act and behave as if we are in for a drink like ordinary punters and we'll see what's what," says Spotter. "When the Richardsons come in, let them make the first move because you can bet all the tea in china they will ask us who we are and what business we have on their patch."

After travelling across London they arrive at The Craven Arms, just as it is opening and the three of them walk in. Tucker orders three pints of bitter and brings them over to the table. Silver asks what sort of drink it is.

"Look just drink it. It's just so they don't know we're Irishmen. If we had three pints of Guinness in front of us they would be wide for us." The three men are sitting yarning away when the two Richardsons walk in and Spotter nods to Silver and gives tucker a light kick under the table. After ordering their drink the Richardsons start looking at the three men, and are trying to make conversation with them.

"Are you boys off to Epsom races today, or are you heading to the Old Bailey?" Both brothers laugh.

"No we're just waiting on a friend coming in, and then we're gone," says Spotter.

"Don't I know you?" asks Eddie Richardson "You're Spotter the Belfast man from the Edgeware Road, aren't you? You're a bit off your patch over here."

"Yes I'm doing a bit of business with a guy from this neck of the woods. Just waiting on him coming in, get the few quid and that's us gone."

"So you think you can come over to our patch and do business without our okay and just walk away."

"Look fellows," says Spotter, "it's simple as this. The guy's only meeting us here. We're not really doing business on your patch. We know the score and we're not treading on your toes."

Bobby, the other brother chips in, "I don't like you Irishmen and I don't like you drinking in our local." Silver is getting agitated and is rapping the table as his nerves are getting the better of him. "And who the fuck is the drummer and the quiet man? Are they your minders." Both brothers laugh. Just at that Silver jumps up and smashes a right hand into Bobby's face and knocks him cold.

He then grabs Eddie and tells him that he's here to collect for John Walsh.

"In case you've lost your memory, it's the money you two stole on him and if I don't get it I will kill you two cardboard gangsters." Silver then throws Eddie out of his way. "We were going to try it the nice way. Now it's the only way. Get the money or I will personally break both your necks." Spotter and Tucker pull Silver back and the three men leave the pub. Outside they hail a cab and get into it.

"That's it. You may get out of town Silver. I told you to play it my way but you're pig headed," says Spotter.

"Look boys. Anything I ever done, I done on my own. I appreciate you coming with me but if I can't do it myself. I won't ask anyone else to do it."

Tucker butts in and tries to explain to Silver that this isn't Belfast and that it's a completely different story over here. Silver calms down and tells the two men that he couldn't listen anymore to them two pricks.

"Look, go back to Mary Anne's and wait for a few days till we find out what way the land lies." The taxi pulls up at Woodstock Grove and Silver gets out.

"We will be over in a day or two just lay low and we will see if we can fix it up. I will ring Mary when we are coming but I'm warning you Silver. Stay handy. Don't go wandering around London, you could end up in the Thames."

A couple of days later Spotter and Tucker arrive at the lodgings and walk in and Silver is sitting in the living room talking to Mary Anne.

"Can we have a few minutes Mary. We need to talk a bit of business with Paddy."

"I'll make a mouthful of tea. Then you can have a bit of privacy. I'm going to the shop soon.

I will be out for a while." Mary duly makes the tea and then puts on her coat and heads out the door.

"Now look Paddy, we have arranged a sit down with them two Richardsons and they say they will make you an offer. I think they said twenty grand and that would be the end of it,"says Spotter.

"Do you think I'm going to walk into the lion's den with them boys; I'd be putting my spoon in the wrong stew there."

"No, I thought of all that. The meeting is going to be in a nightclub where everyone can see what's going on. We will be team handed; another couple of friends of mine is going with us. They won't try anything smart. So Friday night get your self geared up, and we will call for you at eight o'clock. And try and keep a cool head.What do you think?" asks Spotter. "I will have a heater with me. It's just in case. You know what I mean," says Tucker.

"In the name of God what have I got myself into? I'm going to get drunk," says Silver.

"Look, Paddy. The Stagecoach bar or the Waterloo are alright. So if you have a few drinks in there nobody will even know you're there but be sober for Friday night."

Chapter 10

Friday night arrives. Silver is standing outside Mary Anne's and two black taxis pull up and Spotter shouts out of one of them for Silver to get in. Silver climbs in the back seat and Tucker is sitting there along side two other men; Todd and Jimmy. Spotter tells him that there are four other men in the other taxi, as they couldn't go to face the Richardson's in their bare feet so to speak. Tucker introduces Silver to Todd and Jimmy, two hard men in their own right but not just on par with Silver. After a few minutes they pull up outside the Stork Club in central London. The others get out of the second taxi and are introduced to Silver: Danny O, Billy B, Paddy F who has come down from Birmingham along with his mate Peezer. No second names are discussed but they all know or have heard of Silver and he's from Belfast, and that means they stand by each other. Spotter starts explaining what the situation is and that the Richardson's have agreed to pay and if they do there is a few quid in it for everyone. Spotter asks Tucker has he got the heater ready and Tucker presses on his pocket and nods.

"Okay. No rowdy stuff. We will all have a drink and see how the lay of the land sits and if it pans out okay we will go back over to the Edgeware Road and have a good gargle." Everyone agrees, but this is all new to Silver. It's his first time in England and he always fought on his own but Spotter has told him he needs to go team handed to make an impression. After a little difficulty at the door the men make their way into the nightclub, which would be better known as a clip joint. The drink is exorbitantly expensive and it's about so far way from what Silver is used to in the Black Bull, it is making him feel uneasy. As the boys settle down and take their seats, Spotter calls a waiter and orders a drink. A few minutes later the waiter comes back with the drink and tells the company that the drink is on the house. Spotter asks who paid for it, and the waiter points to Bobby Richardson. "Well, that's a few quid saved on expenses anyway." After a few minutes Bobby is joined by his brother and about eight other men and after another couple of minutes one of the men comes over and asks Silver would he come over for a sit down with his boss? Silver duly obliges and walks over and takes a seat beside Bobby and his brother and they get involved in a heated argument. As Silver gets up to leave, Bobby Richardson attacks him from behind. The Belfast crowd see this and charge across the room and a free for all ensues. Silver is rolling about on the floor and Bobby is kicking him as he tries to get up. Spotter is fighting the other Richardson and the rest of the boys are in the middle of the mob throwing lefts and rights and there is blood flying all over the place. Silver by chance gets up on his feet and he knocks Bobby out with one dig and then gets stuck into the melee and there is what can only described as a free for all. Suddenly another two men walk in with baseball bats and a few iron bars and start distributing them among the Richardsons gang and the brawl is starting to look bad for the Belfast men when Tucker pulls out a gun and fires it into the opposition and takes a step back. By this time Silver is brawling with another of the Richardsons and he let's a yell out of him and falls to the ground. Tucker fires another shot into the ceiling and the Richardson's gang start making themselves scarce. Spotter runs over to Silver and asks him what's wrong and Silver tells him he's being shot in the leg and could someone call an ambulance.

"We will have to make ourselves scarce before the cops come but he would call an ambulance when he got out of the club." Everyone disperses and Silver is left lying on the floor with the blood flowing profusely from his wound.

"What have I got myself into here. Guns, iron bars, and baseball bats; this isn't my scene. I wish I was back in Belfast." Within minutes the club is swarming with cops and medics who are now attending to Silver's leg wound.

A senior cop walks over to Silver and asks him what happened and he replies, "Your guess is as good as mine. I was sitting here minding my own business and I got shot. What sort of a country is this?"

"Well mister, I'd watch what company you keep from now on and I'm sure you won't get shot again. By the way, what's your name?" The medic interrupts and tells the cop that he must get him to hospital, as the bullet seems to have hit a small but dangerous artery.

"Okay. We will follow you back to the hospital but tell whoever is in charge there that this man is under arrest and hasn't to be released no matter what he says, not until we interview him at least." Silver is placed on a stretcher and carried out and put in an ambulance and the senior cop points to a young policeman and tells him to accompany the man in the ambulance and not to let him out of his sight.

A few hours later Silver is sitting in bed with his leg in traction as they found that his leg was also broken and told him he would be off his feet for six weeks. At that stage the Senior cop walks in along with a plainclothes detective and they take a seat at each side of Silver's bed.

After some unimportant questions the detective asks Silver straight out, "did the IRA do this?"

Silver laughs."This is London son. The IRA is in Ireland. I just happened to be in the wrong place at the wrong time."

The cop asks him, "is Patrick Joseph McKee your real name and are you known by any other name?"

"What do you mean?" asks Silver.

"Well, we've been in touch with Belfast and although you fit the description they say if you're the man you're supposed to be. You will know the name we are talking about." I suppose you mean 'Silver.' The two cops look at each other and nod.

"Well, at least it's not the IRA we are dealing with Mr. McKee. We will be checking up on you and when we have finished with inquires into what happened, we will be back in touch. So don't be going anywhere fast Mister McKee."

"Yeah. I'm going to run away." Both cops smile, "At least you have a sense of humour," says the detective.

* * *

After a few weeks in hospital Silver is back at Mary Anne's and is walking with the aid of a stick. The door knocks and in walks Spotter.

"How you doing Paddy? I got that number you wanted in Belfast; with a lot of difficulty but I have it now. Spotter hands Silver the phone number written on a cigarette packet and he looks at it.

"Is this big Walsh's number. I will give him a ring later." Spotter tells him to ring it now and ask did the Richardsons pay any money to his solicitor because if they did, we want a few quid and you definitely deserve a grand or two for getting one in the leg." "Where's big Tucker?" asks Silver.

"He's afraid to come over after what happened, but I told him it was okay and you know he didn't mean it."

Well tell him if he's coming over don't be bringing any guns near this house."

"Or peelers either," says Mary Anne. Spotter and Silver laugh.

"Can I use your phone Mary?"

"Yes along as you pay for the call, you can use it all day long, but I'm waiting on a wee call from my daughter. As soon as she calls me you can use it after we're finished. I will make you both a cup of tea while your waiting." Mary goes out to the working kitchen and Spotter and Silver get talking.

"What did the coppers ask you Paddy?"

"Well they were happy that there was no IRA involvement and they would investigate what did happen, but I think they were pleased really that it was as they said, gang warfare and I was caught in the middle of it."

Spotter rubs his hands as Mary gives him and Silver a cup of tea.

"When are you going to go home? This week or next?"

"Well I'm hoping big Walsh sends me a few quid to sort youse fellows out and Mary Anne. I owe her a few quid. Then I will probably fly home. I couldn't go on the boat with this leg the way it is. It's hard enough to walk on it, but when the boat it's rocking and rolling all over the place it could break again." Spotter drinks his tea and tells Silver he will be back tomorrow and he can tell him what Walsh said because the Richardsons assured him that they left ten grand with his solicitors. "We're all entitled to something."

"I agree. I will call him and see what's what." Spotter leaves and Mary receives her call, finishes and tells Silver he can make his own call now. He gets up and asks Mary to dial the number and she does and hands the receiver to Silver.

The phone rings for a few minutes and someone on the other end says "hello. Walsh's scrap metal company. Buster speaking."

"Is that Buster Brown speaking?"

"Yes, who is this?"

"It's Silver."

"What about you Silver. Who are you looking?

"I'm looking big John. Is he about?"

"Hold on for a minute. By the way do you know they're knocking Allams sale yard and the rest of the markets down. The fish market is already gone and they're starting on Oxford Street in a few weeks and there'll be none of it left."

"Jesus I may get home. Put big John on quickly. I'm phoning from London. This is costing a fortune." Big John comes on the phone and Silver explains his dilemma and John asks him what does he want him to do.

"What do I want you to do? I got shot trying to get you your money and as far as I'm aware you got ten thousand pounds of what you where owed and your asking me what you should do. I will tell you what to do. I'm going to send Mary down on Friday and you better have at least five hundred quid for her or I will see you when I get home and I won't be laughing."

John tries to calm him down but he is having none of it so he agrees to give Mary the money on Friday but he won't be giving a penny more. Silver hangs up and asks Mary Anne to try and get him the number of the Black Bull in Cromac Street in Belfast. Mary Anne tries but after an exhaustive amount of time an operator tells her that its an ex directory number and under no circumstances can they give the number out to the public. Silver asks Mary Anne to give him a minute to think who has a phone in the Market but he can't think of anyone.

"I've got it! Try Barney Ross scrap merchant. He has a phone and it wont be ex directory."

Mary rings directory inquires and gets the number and dials it for him and hands the receiver to Silver. Silver takes the phone and Barney comes on the phone. "Hello, Silver here Barney."

"How's it going Paddy. I heard about your bad luck across the water. Are you home?"

"No, not yet. I need you to go up to my Mary's family home and give her a message. Can you do it? I need it done before Friday."

"Where does she live?" Silver gives him the address and Barney says he would go up later in the day when the yard isn't so busy.

"All I want you to tell her is to go to Walsh's yard on Friday afternoon and collect five hundred quid off big John."

"You know I don't bother with him Paddy and I don't like anything that involves him. He's wrecked my business here."

"Look, do this favour for me and I will see you right when I get home." After a bit of toing and froing Barney agrees to do the errand for him. "I wouldn't do this for anyone else Paddy, remember that." "I will Barney and thanks." Silver hangs up the phone.

"Now Mary Anne how do I get the air fare out of here? Would you trust me for it and I promise I will send you the money and what I owe you as soon as I get back home."

"I've heard all that before but you know something. I like you Silver and I trust you. I will lend you twenty pounds. I think that should be enough."

Spotter can get you a lift to the airport."

"I've to go to the hospital on Friday or I would go home now but I want this leg right. I don't want be left with a gammy leg for the rest of my life."

* * *

A few days later Silver arrives in a taxi at his home in the Market area and as he is getting out of the taxi he notices that the hall door is open. He pays the driver, bids him good luck, grabs his case and walks into his kitchen and the place is spotless.

After a few minutes the door opens and in walks Mary and the baby. Silver throws his arms around her and then lifts the child and declares "its great to be home again Mary! When did you come back?"

"I'm not coming back. Where did you ever get that idea? I came down and gave this house as good cleaning. Jesus you must have being living like a down and out." Mary opens her bag and hands Silver a large brown envelope. "There's your money. Walsh gave me it after a lot of haggling. Made me feel like a beggar. Never ask me to do that again. He left me standing for over an hour and then he literally threw it at me."

"So Barney Ross went up and gave you the message?"

"Yes, he came up and he also asked me was I all right for a few pounds."

"That was decent of him Mary. So are you going to make a cup of tea." Silver opens his case and pulls out a large box and hands it to Mary. "That's for my baby," and he then hands Mary a small bag, "and that's for you." Mary opens the large box and inside is a beautiful doll and she sets it down beside the child on the settee. She then opens the small bag and inside it is a lovely bracelet.

"Oh thanks, Paddy that's beautiful but I have to tell you I'm not staying."

"What do you mean woman? I need you. My leg isn't working right and I need you to look after me. God I missed you and the child."

"That's as may be but I've got quite used to living with my mum and to be honest if I was coming back you'd have to at least curtail your drinking."

"Look Mary, I promise you I am a changed man and I will definitely watch my drinking."

"Well okay but the first time you come home drunk, the child and me will leave again."

"That's not a problem and now all I'd like is a nice cup of your tea. The tea in England is rotten. You couldn't drink it, its like dish water."

"I got a bap and a bit of cooked ham earlier so I will make you a bap sandwich and you can rest that leg of yours. How is it anyway?"

"The doctor told me before I came away that it would be as right as rain in a few weeks but not to be putting too much weight on it." Just then there is a knock at the door and Mary goes to answer it and in walks Croaky.

"How's it going Paddy? I came round to see how you're keeping. It's all over the district that you're home. The neighbours around here couldn't hold their water, but its good to see you and it's also good to see you and the child Mary."

"Will you have a cup of tea while you're here?"

"Thanks. I will have a wee cup in my hand if you don't mind."

"If I minded I wouldn't be asking you. Do you want anything to eat?"

"No, just a cup of tea in my hand thanks. Well Paddy the Markets are finished. They're starting on the abattoir next week and when that's finished that's it."

"Jesus I'm only a way a few weeks. They didn't waste much time. So what are you and the lads doing for work?"

Croaky shrugs his shoulders, "I bought a wee van and I'm going to do a bit of dealing. I may start selling fowl or do a bit of chugging at the rags or a bit of scrap."

"It seems everyone in the market area is a fowl dealer or a horse dealer," says Silver. "Call around tomorrow. You can run me over to Allams. I want to see what's happening round there."

"I will call for you at about ten in the morning but let me tell you that you'll cry your eyes out. Big man or not, it's the worst I've seen since the war years. It's like a bombsite. Mary brings the tea out and hands Silver the ham bap and hands Croaky a cup of tea.

"After I drink this I will go, and by the way that big fucker Billy McCausland was asking about you last week. He's running about slabbering about you getting shot and that's the end of you as a hard man." Silver puts his finger to his lips signalling Croaky to say no more.

"We'll see about that. I think that big man is a chancer and if I can get to the bottom of what went on, I will kill him if I find out it was him that stroked me.

Mary walks back in from the scullery, "what was that you said Paddy"? "Nothing Mary, I was just saying I still have to go to court about that case last year, the one I got three months for."

"Are we never going to hear the end of that. I thought it was over and done with?"

"It is, but the judge wants to know who owns the money. So among them be it. There's no chance of me getting it. I was the mug who done the time. Fuck me wasn't I a mug."

"Paddy, stop that language in front of the child."

"Sure she is sleeping."

"I don't care. I don't want to hear that language in this house while she is growing up and that's that." Croaky finishes his tea quickly and makes his excuses and leaves. "Your only home and your mates are round at the door. Will we ever get a minute of privacy in this house?"

"What do you mean Mary? Croaky has been running in and out of here for years."

"I know but he should have at least waited until tomorrow to call, if he had any sense.

The next morning Croaky arrives at Silver's house and asks him does he want to walk around to Allams or can he drive him around in his wee van.

"I think we will walk around. I need all the exercise I can get to strengthen up this oul leg."

"Okay, come on, get your coat but be prepared. You're not going to like what you see." Silver and McNally walk around to the markets and as they walk down Oxford Street they turn into the square and the first thing Silver sees is Eastwood's demolition cranes, lorries, and a great big ball that is swinging against a wall, falling like a snowman melting.

"God, what is happening? This is horrible can none of it be saved?"

"This is what they call progress and there is nothing nobody can do about it. It will be waste ground by next week and there will be no work for anyone. They will all be looking jobs in the Bakery and none of our men are going to like that; baking bread and cakes like Mary Baker and her wee buns."

"It's no laugh Croaky. That's our life being demolished away," says Silver.

"Yes, I know but while you were in England getting yourself shot, the boys and me tried everything to try and stop this but to no avail and your telling me it's not funny." A tear is running down Silver's face and he takes out his handkerchief and rubs his face trying to hide the fact that he has shed a tear, something he hasn't done for years.

"Come on, lets get out of here before I do something that may get me into trouble. I'm going for a few pints. Are you going?"

"What to do? Drown your sorrows? You know you let us down Paddy. If you had have been here it may have been different."

"Look, I may be a bit of a rough house but no one could stop this. It's big business and in ten years time you couldn't guess what will be built here. I bet you one thing you can be sure. It won't be houses for us and I bet you, not one market trader will have anything to do with any of the business built here. Come on I'm going for that pint. One will do me no harm and anyway my leg is starting to feel the pinch."

Croaky and Silver walk slowly over to the Black Bull and as soon as they walk in the customers are all up shaking hands with him and welcoming him home. Suddenly the front door flies open and in walks Billy McCausland. He walks straight to Silver.

"I heard you were back. Now next Wednesday we have our last meeting with the barrister. Robinson will be there and we're going to try and work out a way to resolve this. Be there at half ten Wednesday morning."

"Who do you think your talking to? Do you think because I have a gammy leg I couldn't fix you."

"From what I hear you couldn't fix our Aggy and our Aggy's a cat." Silver makes a go for Billy who backs off and runs to the door and stands holding the door open. As he is leaving he shouts at Silver. "I mean it. Be there on

Wednesday. I want this thing over and done with. If you don't come freely I will get the judge to subpoena you. Now do what you like about it; Sheeps Head!" Silver makes a go for Billy but falls over as his leg comes from below him and he has to be helped up by Croaky and a few of the customers. They manage to get Silver a chair and he sits down. He is out of breath and he is shaking.

"I'm going to fix that big fucker and I'm going to hurt him. Nobody calls me Sheeps Head and gets away with it. Nobody."

Chapter 11

A few days later there's a knock at Silver's door and he opens it. Barney Ross is standing there. "Hello Barney. Sorry I haven't been around to see you to thank you for going to give Mary that message."

"That's not a problem. Glad to do anyone in trouble a favour. By the way how is Mary and the child getting on?" Silver invites him in and Barney declines. "I came around to ask you to do me a favour."

Silver looks at him and is just about to say, 'you get nothing for nothing' but he holds his tongue. "What can I do for you Barney?"

"Young Michael is going to Armagh point to point on Saturday and I can't go up with him. I was wondering if you would tag along with him and keep an eye on things. It's his first day delivering the bookies gear and the boxes and he would need a hand and you'll get a fiver for the day. So all I have to do is go with him in the van and give him a hand to unload the bookies gear. That's it but he's a bit windy. We have never done Armagh point before and well you know what I mean."

"I know rightly what you mean. Someone else maybe looking after the bookies joints and won't let him operate. So it's not a hand you need, it's a heavy hand you need."

"Well if you want to put it like that but I'm sure there won't be any trouble. You know all the bookies anyway."

"Bottom line – does anyone else have the contract and will he be stepping on anyone's toes."

"Theres a boy called Franco but he's no bother. He will try and supply the boxes that the bookies stand on but we've been doing it for years. So there will be a bit of an argument."

"Your man is not going to take it lying down; if he runs the pitches he's not a fool."

"Look Silver, I need you to go up Saturday morning. I will make it a tenner what do you say?"

"That's no problem. Tell young Michael to call here Saturday morning and the jobs a good'n. And to bring a flask of tea with him."

"He will be here at half eight sharp Silver, no later." Both men shake hands and Silver walks back into the house.

Saturday morning arrives and Silver is sitting waiting on young Michael when he hears a knock at the door. He puts on his coat and shouts up the stairs to Mary that he's away and he will be home about seven o'clock for his tea. Silver walks out and a postman is standing holding a letter and hands it to Silver.

"I need you to sign for this letter please." Silver looks at him and after a few minutes signs his name in a little book.

"What's this for," Silver asks the postman. "I don't know mister, I just deliver the letters. I don't know what's in them sorry but you had to sign your name for it." Silver walks back into the kitchen and opens the letter...

Dear Mr. McKee you are subpoenaed to appear at Belfast crown court on the sixteenth of December. Failure to appear will result in a bench warrant being issued for your arrest.

Silver sticks the letter in his pocket and walks out closing the hall door behind him. A minute later Michael pulls up in and old van and shouts out the window at Silver.

"Sorry I'm a bit late. She was hard to start. Had to get a push but she's alright now. The battery will charge up with the drive."

Silver walks around the van and has a look all round it.

"I suppose she's taxed and insured and you have a license son?"

The tax is only up on her but she's insured and I passed my test a month ago. I've a full licence Mister McKee."

"Call me Paddy, and don't be driving like the devil going through Athlone. Just take it easy. We may get there five minutes later but we've plenty of time and I want to get there in one piece." Silver climbs into the passenger seat and they set off up the road. As they are driving along the road Michael starts asking questions but Silver is dozing and doesn't want to have a conversation.

"My Da says you got shot in London, Paddy, by London gangsters. Is that true?"

Silver gathers himself up and sits up and lights a cigarette. "Well that's half right. I did get shot but not by any gangsters. It was an accident."

"He also said you knocked a bull out with a single punch to the head in Allams."

"What else did your da tell you?"

"He said you're the hardest man he ever seen fighting and that if anything happened up here today you'd sort it out."

"You've just told me what I was thinking all along son."

"What's that Paddy?"

"Nothing son. You wouldn't understand."

"Did you fight Stormy Weatherall up the Shankill?"

"Look, what's your name?"

"Michael, Paddy."

"If you believe all you hear you'll eat all you see. Now can I have a wee bit of peace and quiet. I'm going to have a wee kip. You know something the peelers in London never asked me as many questions."

After about an hour or so Silver wakens up and asks how far they have to go. "I'm not sure. I've never been up here before but they will have markers on the road when we get near the points." Silver lights another cigarette and asks Michael his age. "I'm nineteen Paddy."

"Nineteen and you're driving. I suppose you have a girl as well."

"I'm getting married next year."

"For God's sake, you're only out of nappies and you're getting married."

"You're living in the old days, Paddy, everybody is getting married now at twenty and twenty-one. It's the done thing."

"So tell me, who is this guy Franco?"

"He's a bookie from Dungannon and he's trying to move in on our business. We have been doing this for years and years my da and our Harry were doing this job in all the other point to points but we never done Armagh so it's all new to me."

"I suppose your da told you why I was coming with you?"

"Yes, he said that you would fix Franco and anybody else that caused any trouble."

"Yes, you wouldn't have to be a mind reader to know that. Slow down... there's a wee sign saying point to point so drive slow. It mustn't be far". About a mile up the road they pull into the field where the point to point is being held. They ask one of the stewards where the bookmakers are standing. The steward points to two lines taped off and says... "each side of that tape." Silver tells Michael to pull up behind the tapes. As they pull up some of the Belfast bookies come over and start sorting out their stands and bookie bags and start erecting their joints.

One of the bookies called Connolly Quinn comes over and lifts his tripod and looks at Silver. "What has you away up here today, Paddy?"

"Hello Quinny, long time no see. I'm just up helping the young lad. His da had business to do in Belfast so he couldn't come with him and he asked me to give him a hand."

"Will you do outside man for me? My man couldn't come either, but it's more to do with drink than business."

"I wouldn't be too fast on my feet since I got the leg hurt but I will give you a show of the betting if that will do you."

"That's all I need. I won't be having any bets back so you won't have to run all over the place."

"Okay. When I'm finished helping young Ross I will be over to see you."

"That's okay. I'm going to have a cup of tea."

"That's not a bad idea. I think I will have one myself with young Ross. I'll be over when I'm finished."

After Silver and Michael have their tea, the first race is about to get underway. Silver is standing calling the betting to Quinn and the punters are queuing up to have a bet with him. Quinn is shouting at the top of his voice, "evens threes bar!" The punters are lashing the money on the even money favourite and Quinn is laying them all. The other bookmakers are hardly taking a bet and some are getting annoyed at Quinn and some are shouting at him to shorten the odds but Quinn is laying everyone evens. The starter calls the runners in, waves his white flag and they're off and running. After the first circuit the favourite is leading by about six lengths and Quinn is getting worried looking and jumps down from his box and walks over to Silver.

"If this wins I'm in trouble!" he tells Silver.

"What do you mean?"

"I will tell you what I mean. I haven't the money to pay the punters out."

"Fuck me man, why did you lay them if you can't pay them."

"You wouldn't understand, anyway. I'm going to the toilet. Mind the joint and don't worry, I have the money in my pocket." As the horses are turning around the top bend Quinn is now sitting in his car and he has his head out the window listening to the public address system. Silver danders down to him and asks him what the hell he is playing at.

"I'll tell you what I'm playing at. If this favourite wins I'm driving down that road. You can come with me if you want but I'm leaving." As the favourite heads towards the penultimate fence he inexplicably pulls up and the outsider runs on jumps the last and wins the race. Quinn gets out of the car and is full of confidence now and walks back to his stand to sounds of booing coming from the crowd.

"You're a bastard Quinn. You hired me today just in case you couldn't get away, if the favourite won and me like a mug fell for it."

"The favourite was never going to win. I have the jockey in my pocket. I was just a bit worried."

"You were that worried you were going to drive down the road and leave me to the crowd.

Quinn puts his hand in his pocket and pulls out a ten-pound note and hands it to Silver.

"Here! I don't need you now. You're well paid now. Go on over to young Ross and help him."

"Who do you think your talking to Quinn, some mug?"

"Look Silver, go away or I will get Stormy to fix you. Just like the night he knocked your bollox in up the Shankill. You weren't such a big fellow that night." Silver makes a go for Quinn but a policeman walks over.

"Everything all right with you two?"

"Yes, just a little disagreement over a bet but its all sorted now Sir. I just paid him now I'm away to get ready for the second race." Silver walks over to Michael's van and asks is their any more tea left.

"Yes, the flask is in the front seat. Help yourself to a sandwich as well." Silver is sitting in the van drinking his tea when two men knock on the window.

"Is this your van?"

"No, that lad there owns it." Silver points to Michael.

"He's just a kid. Who's the boss here?"

"He is. Why is there something wrong?"

"Well if he's the boss, it's got nothing to do with you. You just sit there and enjoy your tea and mind your own business." The two men walk over to Michael and start questioning him.

"Who told you that you could just arrive up here from Belfast and start taking over our pitches?"

"My da has being doing the points for a lifetime and it's our business. We supply the boxes and deliver the bookmakers joints and bags. We've being doing it for years."

"Well you won't be doing it anymore and if you have any sense you'll pack up your wee van and head on home to Frankie town or the Mc Cooey's or whatever you call it in Belfast." Both men burst out laughing at their own joke. Michael shouts for Paddy and hearing him he gets out of the van and walks down to where the three of them are standing.

"What's going on here?"

"Look didn't you say he's the boss, so as I told you ten minutes ago mind your own business for your own sake."

"They said we've to pack up and leave Silver." "What did you say?" asks one of the tough guys.

"I told him we have to leave."

One of the tough guys looks at the other and mumbles, "it couldn't be him." "It couldn't be who?" asks Silver.

"Nobody, just pack up and leave for your own safety and don't come back."

"I'm going to tell you two guys a wee story and then I'm going to stop talking Now listen."

"Who do you think you are? This is Armagh and I'm Franco Mc Donnell from Portadown and this is my mate Tommy Fleming."

"And what! says Silver abruptly. "So let me continue. This will only take a minute. Is there a public phone about here? asks Silver.

"Yes, there's one in the pub at the crossroads about half a mile down the road." "Good now I want one of you or even the two of you to go and phone a good friend of mine called P.G. McQuaid. He lives in Dungannon. In fact he's an Armagh man, and just tell him that I'm here."

"So who will we tell him is here. Not that we're going to phone him. Do you think we're message boys."

"Just tell him Paddy Joe McKee is here and he needs him to come over for a few minutes and while you're there call an ambulance because if you two come back here today you'll be needing one."

"Jesus, it is Silver McKee. I've heard P.G. talking about you a million times. Jesus, we're sorry Silver. Look let's forget everything we said and we will be on our way."

"No problem boys now. I'm going to finish off my tea. Tell the young lad you're sorry for annoying him and we'll let bygones be bygones. Now good day and good luck."

"Thanks Silver."

"It's Paddy. Only my closest friends call me Silver. Sorry Mister McKee we're away on about our business." After a couple of hours the bookmakers are packing their gear into the van and a few of them are slipping Silver a few bob when Quinn walks over and hands his joint to Michael. Silver ignores him until he loads his stuff in the van. Then follows him down to his car and gives him a tug on the shoulder.

"I will be home tonight and I'm going looking for Stormy and I will be telling him that you're running around telling people that he's going to do me and that he done me up the Shankill. I think he might just come looking you."

"Look Silver. He doesn't like you and neither do I. You're a has been. Going over to London to take on the gangsters. That's a joke. They sent you home in an ambulance. Your days of being a hard man are well and truly over."

"You know something Quinn. I'd hit you a dig on the jaw but I won't. Do you want to know why? I will tell you why. I might kill you and I don't want to go to jail over you or any other fuckpot like you. Now get into that car and take yourself off and keep out of my way in Belfast because I may not always be in so good a mood."

Quinn gets into the car, starts the engine and as he is driving off he shouts,

"I will be backing Stormy. You can have a free bet you mug. Silver makes a go as if to run after the car and Quinn speeds off.

Silver walks over to Michael. "Are we near ready to leave because if I don't leave soon I will hurt someone? I feel like I've been used and abused this day but I can assure you young Ross, it won't happen again." Silver and Michael get into the van and drive out of the field and head towards home. As they are nearing home Michael says, "can I ask you a question Paddy?"

"Yes, what do you want to know, as long as it isn't going to be the third degree?"

"If you feel the way you do, why do you let people make a mug out of you? Your words not mine Paddy."

"It's like this son. All my life it's been about doing favours and helping people out of trouble. I never started a fight in my life. You know it was always someone else's doing; be it by talk or me saving his or her bacon. For example, your Da done me a favour when I was in England,so I'm returning it by coming here today with you. Do you think I enjoy standing in a field all day mucked to the gutters?"

"I know, but your man the bookie Quinn, he made an idiot out of you in front of people and was laughing at you?Why did you not slap him?"

"If I had hit him the cops would have been on me like bees around honey and I would be back in jail and Quinn, the respectable bookie, would be told to go about his business."

"But I have heard loads of stories about you and it seems that all your life you have been the fall guy. A lot of people around you got into trade and business but you remained a simple cattle drover and now there's no markets. It seems like your days are over."

Silver sits quiet for a few minutes and looks at Michael sternly. "A few years ago I would have slapped your face for talking to me like that but I've learnt something from you today?"

"What's that?" asks Michael excitedly, thinking he has said something profound to Silver.

"I tell you what you said son. Nothing. It's the way you young people and business people act. It's every man for themselves. All you done was remind me that I was born and reared into a different world where people helped each other genuinely and looked after each other. Not any more. It's dog eat dog and I really don't feel part of that world. You know I had my chances. I could have thrown my weight about and got a few quid but in a way you are right. I was always looking after other people and never looked after those closest to me, namely my wife and child. I dread what kind of world my daughter is going to grow up into but you have got me thinking. I'm going to look after myself from now on. Patrick Joseph McKee will be looking after number one."

The van stops outside Silver's house and he gets out and walks around to the driver's side and shakes hands with Michael. "Maybe, just maybe, I did learn something today from you. Man mind thyself."

Silver walks into the house and as soon as he walks in Mary is acting in a mood. "Half eight at night. What time is this to come in for you dinner. You'll be asking me to bring it around to the pub next."

"Look Mary, I've been working at a point to point and I'm only home this minute. Look at my boots. Do you think I'd get all that muck in the Black Bull?" Mary walks into the scullery and comes out with a plate of cabbage and ribs, Silver's favourite meal and sets it down in front of him.

"You know something, Mary. It's the simple things in life that are important. By the way where's the child. She's in bed sleeping. Where do you think she - is out playing tennis or something? So don't be shouting. It took me all night to get her to settled so if she wakens you can nurse her. I'm exhausted and as soon as you finish your dinner I'm going to my bed. You can sit there all night if you want, but don't be putting that radio on because you play it that loud the whole street can hear it."

"Mary, for Gods sake, give my head peace will you? I'm tired myself. I was working all day."

"You could have fooled me. I thought horse racing was an enjoyable day out for men?" "It is, but not if your working."

Chapter 12

Billy and Harry are sitting in the court chambers talking to their respective barristers and trying to work out a deal as to how to get the money and deeds back from the courts. Bob who represents Billy implies to Harry's barrister that the judge could confiscate the money but it would be highly unusual, but he could. Unless the two parties come to a general agreement endorsed on council's brief, it could go any way. Billy interrupts and says that all he wants is his deeds back and a thousand pounds and he will be happy.

"I know you would be Billy but I put ten thousand in and I want ten thousand back. Why should I lose a grand out of my money?" says Harry.

"Look here, Harry, I didn't put the counterfeit money in the case and I have to get something back. Like fair play is good sport."

"What about this man McKee? Could he have done it?"

"To be honest I don't Silver would have the brains to do it. Or the wherewithal. He is a nuisance at times."

"Why has he not came to the last two consultations? The judge may ask him for an explanation" remarks Harry's barrister.

"He can be a very difficult man. Took himself away to London and got himself shot does that not say it all."

"Ah!" says Bob, "now we have a link. Who shot him?"

"Seems it was the London gangsters," says Billy, "but nobody was charged with it. I find that strange."

"There's your answer. He must have got the counterfeit money from them. That's our case. All we have to do now is iron out an agreement between our two parties and that will be the end of it."

Harry chirps in. "That sounds all very simple but I stand to lose a grand and six our eight months interest on ten grand it's no laughing matter."

The two barristers ask the two men to give them a bit of privacy for ten minutes and they will call them back when they're ready. After a few minutes Bob comes out into the court halls and walks over to Harry and Billy.

"Look we have patched up a deal here which will be good for both of you. I will explain it over in the chambers. Follow me please." The three men enter the room and sit with Harry's counsel who reads out a prepared statement that they have formulated.

"No! I'm not having that! That means I lose, Billy gets his deeds and a thousand pounds of my money. What is this, a get up?"

"Let me make it clearer to you. Both parties. If we go into court, my fees will run into a thousand pounds and the same for Billy. If we quit now and present this to the court on the sixteenth of December our combined costs will be a thousand so its up to you men now. But take my advice shake hands and get back to your work because if this starts to get messy you could maybe, just maybe, be a lot more out of pocket."

"I'm up for it," says Billy. "If I were in your position I'd be doing the same. Your coming out losing nothing. I put two grand in. I'm losing a grand," says Billy.

"Yes but was it real money?" chirps Harry.

Billy gets up out of his chair, "That's it; I've had enough. We'll leave it up to the judge." Bob tells Billy to sit down and not to be taking things personal. Billy reluctantly sits down and listens to both barristers. After some haggling both men agree on the joint strategy put forward by the barristers and each sign the agreement.

"Now we are agreed that the line we take is, McKee must have switched the money and he probably acquired it in England but I don't think it will get to that. The judge will probably be satisfied with the terms agreed on Counsel brief. McKee will be a by the by. In fact he probably doesn't even have to be here. "Well he got a subpoena because I got the court to send it. If he's going to be the fall guy, I want you to hammer it home that he caused all of this bother."

"Look this isn't a criminal case. So all it will do is blacken his name."

"That's what I want," says Billy.

"And me as well, says Harry, "he's been a bit of a thorn in my side for a while. This will put him in his place. The days of the hard men are over. Caput!"

* * *

A few days later as Silver is walking trough the town and he runs into Harry Robinson.

"How's it going Paddy? You should have taken that job with me when I offered you it. Now you've a gamey leg. You've been to prison and things don't look good for you. Let me ask you a question?"

"Go ahead, what do you want to know?

"Who do you think switched the money?"

"That's the sixty-four thousand dollar question and to be honest I don't know."

"Big McCausland I think, but he was with you. I told him you wouldn't do anything like that your too honest and how would you get your hands on counterfeit money? Come on and I'll buy you a drink for old times sake. Let bygones be bygones." The two men walk into the pub and Harry orders two whiskeys and two bottles of stout. Silver takes a gulp out of the stout then downs the whiskey.

"That's the first I've had in a few days. I needed that. Do you know I got a letter to appear at court in December?"

"Yes I know. Big McCausland done that. He's no good Silver and he doesn't like you. Him and that Connolly Quinn fellow were talking about you on Sunday in the club. They said you where finished and that they were going to give Stormy a few quid to fix you." After a few more drinks Silver is half drunk and he tells Harry that he's going to sort Stormy out.

"Who does he think he is? I thought he was my friend but a few people have told me that he was slabbering about me." Harry entices Silver to have a few more drinks and when he gets him drunk he suggests to Silver that he would drive him up to see Stormy and get it sorted out.

Unnoticed by Silver, Harry isn't drinking as much as him and is a lot more sober than Silver who is now near drunk.

"Come on, I'll run you up to the Shankill and you can have it out with him, and that will put it all to bed once and for all."

"Lets go. I'm your man. I'll settle this once and for all. Then I will get the hold of Quinn and McCausland and I'll beat the crap out of both of them." Both men walk to Harry's car and get in, and drive off towards the Shankill. They pull up outside the Rex bar and both get out and walk in.

After ordering a drink Harry asks, "Is Stormy about?"

"Who's looking him?" asks a man at the end of the bar?

"I'm looking him, Silver McKee. Tell him I'm looking him and I want to have it out with him once and for all."

"Well, he's working shifts down in Isaac Andrews flourmill, but I will tell him you where here looking him if you want."

"Yes, you do that for me," says Harry. Silver goes to the toilet and when he comes back there's no sign of Harry.

"Your friend's away on mister and I suggest you follow him."

"Who do you think your talking to; do you know who I am?"

"I'll be quite honest with you mister, I don't really care. I'm just advising you to leave and follow that big mouthed fucker who was with you."

"Why what did he say?"

"He said that you where up here to start trouble with Stormy and this is Stormy's local. So before the crowd starts to come in, it would be in your best interests to leave." The bar man comes from behind the bar, "in fact you're leaving now whether you like it or not. The last night you were in here you started a row. Now it's time to go. Finish your drink and be on your way." Silver lifts his drink gulps it down and walks out cursing Harry for leaving him.

* * *

A few days later Silver is up the Falls Road and he calls to see big Kane in his yard in Albert Street. As he is walking up the yard he meets an old friend, Maurice Mc Corry who has worked in the yard for years.

"Is the big man about? asks Silver.

"He's in the office, Paddy, probably stuck beside the fire, where anybody sensible would be. It's freezing today." Down the yard walks Hack Kerr and he shakes hands with Silver and invites him up to the brass shed, as it was called for a cup of tea. All the men are sitting around a brazier – a large fire full of glowing coke and the yarns have started. Dan Braniff asks Silver if he remembered the day when he pushed a wee lorry he was driving which had broken down in the middle of the town. "Remember it, Dan, I've never been right since it. My shoulders were never the same. That was Hunters Stout is Sticking Out you were driving for then."

"Yes but you pushed it on your own and got me started. I never forgot it. Those were the days."

"I wouldn't be fit for it now Dan. I'm getting old now." Maurice throws Silver a penny and as Silver catches it Maurice tells him he hasn't slowed down that much. "Can you still bend it Paddy? Go ahead, give it a go!" and all the others egg Silver on. Two or three minutes later Silver throws it back to Maurice.

"There you can keep that as a souvenir or straighten it out and spend it.

Hack asks, "What the hell where you doing in London Paddy? That's no place for the likes of us. They're a different breed from us. Shooting people? Where will it all end."

"I'll tell you where it all ended. Me with a gamey leg and no work to go to. Do you think Big Kane would give me a start? I could do with a change of luck and I'm skint into the bargain."

"You'll never have anything Paddy while your drinking. John Barleycorn will rule the roost."

"How long are you off it Hack?"

"About ten years and you know something. I never miss it. Big Kane must be off it a long while and he's done all right."

Suddenly the sound of Big Kane's boots with the steel clickers on the heels can be heard coming up the yard and Dan, Hack and Maurice scatter and grab some tools as if they've been working away.

"Hello Paddy, how's things? What has you up the Falls; nothing doing at the markets?"

"The markets is finished. Sure it's demolished and there's not a shilling to be earned. It's hard times. Even the bakery is going."

"Yes but you where always good at getting a living. You could turn your hand."

"It's been a while since I got an honest weeks wages and the wife and child need to be fed.

Can you give me a lay on for a couple of weeks till something turns up?

Kane ponders for a minute. "Maybe... I have a big job starting in Lisburn Gas Works along with Carson and Robinsons and I am starting a few men but they're all young fellows. Robby McCartney's son and Horsey Hughes son are starting on Monday and I think there's about a months work there."

"How would I get to Lisburn every morning?"

"Bud Dorrian will be driving the lorry. I'm sure if you have a yarn with him he will pick you up about Cromac Square."

"I think I'm okay with that. When do I start?"

"Monday morning. I will tell Bud to pick you up at eight o'clock in the square. Then you talk to him about lifting you every other morning and he probably will do that."

" I'll be there. Don't worry about it."

"By the way, what's happening with that case of yours with McCausland and Robinson?"

"It's nothing really to do with me but I got a subpoena to appear at court. I never even heard a word before and then the postman gets me to sign for a letter and that was that. Among them be it I done the time and none of the pair of them looked after me. All they kept saying was that it wasn't their counterfeit money. All I can say is, it definitely wasn't mine. Where in God's Name would I get Mickey Mouse money?"

"Look, you should have been wide for them two. Like when would them two ever do you a turn.?"

"You're right. That Harry fellow brought me up to the Shankill to fight Stormy knowing I was drunk as a skunk. Then what does he do? Fucks off and leaves me."

"What is it they say, rats always leave a sinking ship and you should catch yourself on and stop the drink," says Kane. "Honestly Silver, ask yourself a question. Did you ever get into serious trouble when you were sober?"

"Funny thing you saying that, I was thinking that myself."

"Well there's no use me preaching to you but I'm telling you now, be there at eight on Monday. Buds a bit of a hothead. He won't wait for you."

"Thanks Henry. Any chance of a sub big man till I get my first wages?"

"I knew that was coming." Kane puts his hand in his pocket and pulls out a bundle of money and gives Silver two pound notes. "Here take that. It will get you by. It's not a sub; I'm giving it to you. Go and get a few rations for the house and stay off that drink. This oul job in Lisburn isn't easy work." Silver takes the two-pound notes and spits on it like all dealers do and sticks them in his pocket and dander's down the yard and heads for home.

The next Monday Silver is standing in Cromac Square waiting on Kane's lorry to pick him up when his old friend Croaky walks by.

"Hey boy! You not speaking?" shouts Silver.

"I didn't even see you. Where are you going at this hour of the morning?"

"I'm going to work in Lisburn. I got a few weeks work. What about you, are you doing anything?"

"I'm heading down to the docks to try and get picked on. It's hard work but the pay is good."

"Changed times for us all. How are big Lofty and the rest of the boys doing?"

"Nobody is good. It's hard to change from a cattle drover to a builder's labourer or a van deliveryman or for that matter a bread server. None of our men are built for that type of work, but must do is a good master."

Silver sees Kane's lorry coming up the street and he bids Croaky good morning. When the lorry pulls up he gets on the back along side two young fellows sitting with an old coat thrown over them. "Are youse boys cold?"

"It's freezing back here mister. You'll find out when he gets going down the road." Silver sits with his back to the loading board and one of the young fellows asks him does he work for big Henry Kane or Carson and Robinson.

"Whoever pays me on Friday is whom I work for? I suppose it's big Kane as he gave me the start. By the way I'm Paddy McKee. What's your names?"

"I'm Jim Hughes. You might know my Da. He works down in the abattoir – Horsey Hughes?"

"I know him well. Joe's brother."

"That's him."

"And who are you son?"

"I'm Al McCartney. You mightn't know my Da. He works in the flourmill – Robert McCartney?"

"Of course I know him. A while ago I bought a turkey for him. He had a wee lad with him – must have been your wee brother. Better still he works with an old sparring partner of mine Stormy Weatherall." Both Al and Jim look at each other and smile.

"So you must be Silver McKee, Paddy? You're a legend and the rows you've had with Stormy are the talk of Belfast says Al."

"Don't believe all you hear son. It's all baloney."

"But even my Da says it. You're the hardest man in Belfast," says Jim.

"Enough of that oul talk. What sort of a job is this?"

"We are all on our first day, so it's all new to us but it will get us all a few quid for Christmas."

"You're looking far ahead of yourself son. If I get a few weeks out of this I'll be happy enough."

"Tell us this Paddy, did you do Stormy when you fought him up the Shankill?"

"What can I say? Put it like this; me and Stormy are great friends but he's doing a bit of slabbering about me behind my back and who won. Well I'd say the women of the Shankill. They beat the crap out of me with brushes and shovels and anything they could get their hands on. One oul girl swung on my hair like a banshee, squealing like a pig and I won't tell you what she was calling me but it wasn't nice."

Suddenly the lorry stops and Bud gets out and tells everybody that they have arrived at the job. Out of the cab gets Maurice, Dan and Paddens Walsh who was also on his first day working for Kane.

"So what have we to do?" asks Paddens.

"First things first. Let's go and see the foreman and we will find out what the score is and then I'm away. I'll be back for youse at five o'clock sharp."

"Don't be late!" cries Maurice, "this looks like a god-forsaken place." As the men walk onto the job, all they can see is two large gas tanks and rubble everywhere and the smell of gas is nauseating to the extreme.

"Nobody need light a fag here or they'll blow us all to Kingdom Come," says Silver.

"This place is like hell," says Jim to Al, "it will be hard to stick."

Bud drives off shouting out the window of the lorry..."

Good luck to you but you won't catch me working here. It's like a war zone."

After a hard days work loading scrap on a big lorry, the men are glad when Bud arrives to take them home. Silver arrives home that night and walks into the house and Mary asks "What in the name of God is that smell?"

"It's gas but you'll be all right. It's dead gas they call it."

"Dead gas! The smell of your clothes would kill you! Take them off and throw them over the line in the yard. I don't want the child poisoned." Silver changes his clothes and Mary sets him out his dinner. As he is eating he turns to her and says, "Everything tastes of gas." After struggling to eat his dinner. Silver gets up and goes over to his armchair and within minutes he is fast asleep.

* * *

A few weeks later Silver comes home on a Friday night and goes through his now, usual, routine of taking off his clothes and leaving them over the clothes line in the yard. He has his dinner. He then tells Mary, "I'm finished with that job. I'm sick of the smell. You can't even go into a pub without people telling you that you smell like a gas leak."

"Not to worry. Something will crop up and everything will be okay," says Mary... "the child and me haven't starved a winter yet. We'll get by the three of us." Silver says that he wouldn't mind going for a pint if Mary didn't mind and she looks at him with a grin on her face. "When did it ever matter what I said about you going to the pub? I suppose I will be left sitting watching that television you bought us a few weeks ago because you never seem to watch it." Silver gets up and says he's going to have a shave and rub his face and he would be back at ten o'clock.

"I'll bring you in a fish supper for a cup of tea later. That would be nice but I won't hold my breath waiting on it." Silver laughs and a few minutes later he is heading out the door for the pub.

"Give Anne a good kiss for me Mary."

"Why don't you give her one yourself. You're her father you know. Look, I'm going to bed early. Don't be bringing me in anything from the chippy, I'm not hungry anyway we had a good dinner."

Silver slams the door behind him and heads for the Black Bull. As he is walking in the door he meets Lofty who tells him that there's a guy in the pub looking him.

"Friend or foe?" says Silver, laughing.

"I don't know Paddy, I never met him before but sure you'll find out in a few minutes." Silver bids Lofty goodnight and pushes the door into the pub. As he walks over to bar his mate Croaky stops him and asks him how is everything going?

"Come on, let me get you a few drinks. I got my lying weeks money tonight. I jacked that oul job in. It was really a bad job from the word go, but must do is a good master." Silver orders two drinks for Croaky and himself.

Croaky nudges him and points to a tall man sitting at the other end of the bar. "He's looking for you Paddy and he wouldn't tell anyone what for, or who he is."

"Well, we won't be long finding out. Stand where you are. I'm going to pull him and find out what's what." Silver walks over to the stranger and introduces himself and the man gets up and shakes his hand.

"To be honest, I was expecting something else." "What do you mean by that?" asks Silver.

"My name's Jim and I've started a new business and I needed a few doormen and someone recommended you but in all honesty I thought you where a younger man."

"So what's age got to do with it? But before you answer let me tell you I am not a doorman contrary to what you were told."

"But they say you gain respect wherever you go and I know your past. You have been in some scrapes but by and by you're a straight fellow."

"Enough of the small talk. What is it you're really looking for, mister?

"Let me get you a drink and I will explain the whole story." Jim goes and gets a couple of drinks. They sit down at the top end of the bar and discuss the proposition.

"I'm in the promotion business and I've just taken on the biggest gamble in my life. I've booked a band called The Rolling Stones and I need someone who can look after them."

Silver bursts out laughing. "Is that them long haired beatniks that scream and shout and people call it singing. For God's Sake, man, they'd do my head in."

"Look I have booked them into the Woodbourne House Hotel and their manager is staying in the international around the corner in May street. All I want is for you to make them feel safe and important. They will be here for four days and I want you to protect them. Now let me explain: I want you to protect them from themselves, nothing else."

"You mean you want me to nursemaid them?"

"Call it what you want. There's fifty quid in it for you."

"How much did you say?"

"You heard me. Fifty quid. And all I have to do is look after the group."

Yes and maybe the manager because he likes a wee drink."

So how will all this work out?"

"I will book you into the hotel and you will be there just to make sure they don't wreck the place and get into trouble. After they appear at the Ritz Cinema and get back to the hotel in one piece, your job is over. I have got a few younger guys doing the doors and things like that, but you will be chief whip. Isn't that what they call it?"

"Some call it chief steward or chief whip but I don't know if I'm interested or not." "How does sixty quid sound?

Silver puts his hand out; "I'm your man. So when is this all going to happen?"

"Give me your address and I will collect you on Thursday night and put your best suit on and tie that's all I want. But you have to take charge. Show that you're in charge. Look to be honest Paddy if I don't do this show right, there won't be a second one. So I will call for you at half past seven, Thursday night and please be sober and correct."

Chapter 13

Thursday night arrives and as Mary and Silver are sitting watching Top of the Pops, The Rolling Stones appear on the television and Silver says, "is that the boys I'm going to be looking after Mary? I don't think them young fellows need any looking after; they seem to be nice looking boys. I suppose I will have to try and keep the young girls away from them but in all honesty I don't know what I will be doing." "Just stay off the drink and do as the boss tells you and you will be all right. But knowing you it will be your way or the highway."

"You've a terrible idea of what I'm like but in all honesty Mary you've got me all wrong."

"If that's the case I must be married to a different Paddy Joe McKee." Both laugh as a car horn is sounded. "That must be your man."

"I'm away. Give me a kiss before I go Mary." Silver lifts his wee case and leans over to kiss Mary.

"I wonder would you catch yourself on. You would think you where going away for a month instead of three days."

Silver walks out the door and sees Jim sitting in a car. He beckons Silver to get in and as he gets in the front seat, Jim remarks that he cleans up well. As they are driving up the Falls Road Silver is looking around him and pointing out all his old watering holes and streets where he fought this person and that person. Jim tells him that there will be no fighting in this job, as the lads he is going to be looking after are young gentlemen. Silver goes on to tell Jim that he saw them on Top of the Pops.

Jim says, "Yes, they are flying in tomorrow. They were to come today but they had to promote their new song on the show."

"Do you call that singing mister?"

"Just call me Jim, but remember this: I don't care if they can sing or not, I only want them to fill the ABC Cinema or I'm in a bit of trouble. But in all fairness there are only a few hundred tickets left. So fingers crossed. It will sell out all right. There's only one problem Paddy."

"There's always something, I was wondering what it was. This job sounded too easy."

"It's no big deal but their manager is fond of a drink and he's staying in the International Hotel in May Street and he may be a bit of a nuisance."

"Oh, I know it well. In fact a pal of mine owns it, a guy in the fruit business call Mc Grattan. So he's staying there close to the Ritz picture house and the boys are staying out here, out of the way in the Woodbourne Hotel. All you have to do is keep them, all of them, out of trouble." A few minutes later they arrive at the Woodbourne and are met by Des Davidson the manager and his assistant Jackie Calendar. Jim introduces Silver to both men and tells Des to give Silver whatever he wants but any drink he has, he has to pay for it himself.

"That's fine. Let me show you your room Sir. Des is all excited and is very nervous, The Rolling Stones are staying in the hotel, which usually caters for weddings and dinner dances, rather than pop stars. As Silver enters his room he asks Des if he could get a drink.

"Surely Sir, you can have drink all night. After the bar closes our night porter Sammy will gladly look after you and keep you company down in the lounge. Silver hangs up his clothes and follows Des down to the bar where he orders a bottle of stout and a large whiskey. The barmaid, a big country girl called Lena, puts the drink up and tells Silver that it would be twelve shillings and six pence. Silver looks at her and replies, "I only want a drink. I'm not buying shares in the place. Can you charge it to Room 10, please?"

"That will be fine, Sir." Silver takes his drink from the bar and walks to a large seat and sits down beside two other men enjoying a drink. After a few minutes Silver says to one of them, "Sorry for interrupting you, but don't you trade out of St George's Market?"

The man looks at Silver, "yes I do, I own Benner Fruit and I'm a director of this hotel and come to think about it I've seen you about the markets".

"Yes, my name is Paddy McKee. I live in the Market."

"Can I ask you what has you up here in the hotel?"

"I'm doing a job for a fellow. He has a few friends coming to stay here tomorrow and I have the job of looking after them."

"Are they coming to a wedding or on business?"

"No. They're coming over here to sing."

Frank Benner looks at Silver. "I didn't know there was any singing going on in the hotel. It's all new to me. I will have to talk to the manager. We don't have an entertainment licence except for weddings and the odd dinner dance on Saturday nights. But you do look very familiar to me.

Perhaps we have done business or met socially."

Silver gets up to get another drink and says back to Frank, "Somehow or another I don't think so."

After a few minutes Des walks through the lounge and Frank calls him and whispers to him.

Des then tells him that The Rolling Stones are staying in the hotel and none of the staff even know.

"It's supposed to be kept private and confidential."

"And whose your man there. What's he got to do with it all? He's a bit coarse for here, is he not?"

"He's what they call the minder; he's here to keep them under control."

"Oh I see! I thought he seemed a little out of place. Even Terry here said he looked a bit rough."

"Yes, they call him Goldie or Silver or something."

"What?" says Terry!

"Yes. Some nickname I never heard tell of it before. As I say, some precious metal, Gold or Silver or something."

"His proper name is Paddy." Frank tells Des to get Paddy a drink and he then beckons Paddy over and asks him would he like to join him and Terry for a drink. Silver sits down and says that it would be nice to have a little company, as it would be a long night.

"So you're Silver McKee," says Terry, "I've heard that many stories I could write a book about you."

"And so have I," mutters Frank. Even my father spoke of you with respect. He said you where the hardest street fighting man in Ireland."

Silver laughs. "All I can say in answer to you two men is that if all the stories where true I'd either be a millionaire or the heavy weight champion of the world." The three men laugh as Des comes over and sets down a drink in front of Silver.

"Anything this man wants while he's staying here is down to me. Just put it on the Benner account." Des looks at Frank and scratches his head and wonders what has just changed in ten minutes.

A few hours later the bar closes and Terry and Frank order a taxi but not before telling Silver that it was a pleasure to be in his company and they hoped they could do it again sometime. Terry and Frank leave and Silver is sitting in the lounge half drunk when the night porter Sammy appears.

Silver calls him over and tells him to have a seat to sit and talk to him.

"I'm not allowed to sit with the customer's Sir."

"Do you know those two men I was drinking with?"

"Yes. Frank Benner and Terry Mc Comb: both are directors of the hotel."

"Yes, I know they are and they told me that when you came on duty you where to keep me company until I go to bed."

"Well, if they said it would be all right, I suppose it will be okay".

"Do you take a wee gargle son?"

"I wouldn't mind a wee scotch on the fly."

"Well go you and get two whiskeys and two bottles of stout and join me. Put it down to room ten." Sammy gets up and heads around to his dispensary bar and comes back with two whiskeys and tells Silver he can't get the stout, as the big bar was closed.

"That's okay. Sit down and give us a bit of your craic and tell me about yourself. I'm sick sore and tired of people asking about me. I'd like to hear about you." After a few hours of exchanging stories and a few drinks Sammy helps a now drunk Silver up to his room.

* * *

Next morning Silver is fast asleep when he hears the door being knocked. As he awakens he starts to look around and he isn't sure for a few minutes where he is. He shouts to whoever is knocking at the door that he is awake and is getting ready and he will be down in ten minutes. After a bath and a shave Silver gets dressed and heads down to the restaurant for some breakfast and Jim the promoter meets him.

"The Stones will be here at eleven o'clock. So get a bite to eat and get yourself organised. I don't think there will be any fans but you never know. What do you mean the Stones will be here at eleven o'clock, Jim?"

Jim laughs. "I mean The Rolling Stones, the boys you are going to look after."

"Oh yes. I have you now – the beatnick fellows." Silver goes into the restaurant and has breakfast and comes back out to the lounge to await the arrival of the group. Silver is sitting reading The Irish News when suddenly there is a bit of commotion and he jumps up from his chair and there in front of him are the boys themselves. The Rolling Stones, mean really nothing to Silver, who would be more of a Mario Lanza fan, but he has to look after them so he better get to know them. Jim calls Silver and he introduces him to Mick, Brian, Keith, Bill, and Charley.

"This is Patrick. He prefers to be called Paddy and he will look after you and keep uninvited guests from bothering you. He will be close at hand at all times. What happened Andrew?" Jim asks Mick.

"He went on into Belfast city centre. He wants to look after things on the business side. He will be in the Ritz cinema most of the day getting things set up for us to do a sound check later."

"Well, I will leave you in the hands of Paddy here but hopefully you won't need him. No one seems to know you are staying here."

"What?" says Mick, "no one knows that The Stones are in town?"

"No," replies Jim, "we thought it better to give you a bit of rest time, now I have to go." Suddenly a large number of people appear in the lounge, cameramen, sound men and the whole entourage have now taken over the whole front lounge of the hotel. Now all the staff are joining in and there is bedlam in the hotel. Silver just backs off and takes a chair and sits in the background watching. Silver calls a waiter and asks him his name first and then asks him what's all the excitement about.

"You call me Sean Dillon. I'm glad I'm working today that's The Rolling Stones, Mister, they're bigger than the Beatles."

"I'm as wise as ever but all I want is a drink son. Could you get me a bottle of stout and a small whiskey and put it down to room ten. Sean goes and gets the drink and in all the mayhem, the Stones leave the hotel along with a camera crew and as Silver tries to get the drink into him, they are gone and are running down the car park of the hotel. As he is running after them they board a bus. The bus takes off and Silver is lucky as he grabs hold of the passenger bar and walks up to Mick and asks him what he's doing.

"We're having a laugh Paddy. It's no use being in Belfast if everyone doesn't know we're here." Paddy scratches his head and takes a seat but no sooner has he sat down when they were all getting off at the next stop and running up the Stewartstown Road.

"To hell with this I'll take my time walking back to the hotel. I didn't sign up for all this razzmatazz." A few minutes later Silver arrives back at the hotel and Mick is sitting on a settee in the hall lounge. Silver sits beside him and asks him would he like a drink.

"Yes. I'll have hot white rum."

"Hot white rum, is your head cut?"

"Well you asked me did I want a drink and that's what I want." Both laugh. Silver calls Sean and orders the hot white rum and a small whiskey. Sean looks at him and asks did he mean, hot Bacardi rum?

"Yes, that's what I want," says Mick and Sean is over the moon. He is serving a rock and roll giant and Mick Jagger has just spoken to him. After a few drinks and a bit of conversation Mick tells Silver that he is going to go up to his room to relax as they are on stage tonight.

As Mick leaves Brian Jones comes over to Silver and asks, "Is there a television in this hotel".

"Well I haven't seen one and there's none in my room." Sean who is standing close by walks over and tells Brian Jones that the hotel doesn't have a television but the barmaid Lena has a television in her room, as do most of the live-in staff.

"Could you ask her, could I go up and watch it for a half hour, I think we are appearing on the news getting off the plane. I would like to see it, you know what I mean man." Sean goes and asks Lena could she let Brian Jones use her room to watch the local news and Lena is excited and tells Sean it wouldn't be a problem but to let her have five minutes tiding it up before he comes up. Sean walks back to Brian and tells him that he will bring him up in a couple of minutes and Brian says "Cool man."

Sometime later Brian comes back down to the lounge and thanks Sean and informs Silver that a couple of cars or a bus are coming for them at seven o'clock, so could he gather up the rest of the lads and have them all in the hall ready to go. A few minutes later Silver has the whole group sitting nervously in the hall. Silver is talking to them, trying to work out what part he has to play in all this. Then in walks Jim the promoter and calls him.

"Now listen Paddy, all you have to do is make sure they get into the Ritz without any harm.

There will be two other guys to meet you outside the cinema but don't you let anyone of the group out of your sight. Once they are on stage you can sit at the back of the cinema and enjoy the show.

Then it's your job to get them out, without the fans pulling them apart."

"That sounds okay but how many fans do you expect outside the cinema?"

"About a thousand, but they will be all screaming: young teeny boppers and some lads but it is not a tough job, but I need to know that the boys get to that stage without being harmed in any way."

"That's not a problem. So I travel with the boys in the bus and I get them into the Ritz."

"Yes, the cops will be there as well. The three others are all good men. Surely that won't be a problem for you?"

"Whose in charge Jim?"

"You are. You have the final say. Now are you ready?"

"As ready as I'll ever be," Silver scratches his head.

He tells the group to walk behind him to the bus and not to stop for anything, not even to talk to anyone but just keep walking. "When we arrive at the venue, it's the same. I will be in front of you, and you follow and again remember how important it is that you don't stop for any reason." "Okay Paddy, lets go!" chirps Mick. The rest of the group laugh and Silver looks at them. They're all innocent looking lads but he has to babysit them. Silver leads the group out and makes a clear way for them as members of staff and hotel guests line up each side of them. A large crowd has gathered in the car park. As Silver gets to the front door a newspaperman jumps in front of him trying to get an interview from Mick but Silver gently pushes him out of the way. "You can get your story another time but not in my time, sorry." Silver stands at the entrance of the bus as the group board and then he boards and the bus takes off. After a few minutes the bus is driving down the Grosvenor Road and some of the group are shouting out at fellows standing at the corners. Silver gets up and asks the group to take it easy. They will get all the excitement they want later and not to be making it hard for the driver. If they have to stop at the traffic lights there could be trouble. By this time a large crowd are running after the bus. The bus pulls up at the Ritz Cinema and Silver is flabbergasted. He has never seen so many people and the entrances to the Ritz are packed with young and old. As the bus comes to a stop Silver gets to his feet and tells the lads again, "I will lead you through the crowd, and don't stop, keep your heads down and run. The three other minders come over to the bus and form a guard at the doors and Silver tells the group it's time to go. "Don't forget! Don't stop!"

After a few minutes The Stones are in the venue, minus bits of their coats and a few rips, but basically it's a success.

* * *

As the group is doing its performance, Silver decides to go to the Rotunda Restaurant, which is part of the cinema complex for a cup of tea. As he drinks his cup of tea, his head is bursting, listening to girls screaming and the band playing loud music. He sits down beside a young fellow and as usual Silver strikes up a conversation with the stranger. Silver asks him what is his interest in being at the show. He tells him that he is called Andrew Loog Oldham and he is the group's manager. Silver goes on to explain that he is tasked with looking out for the lads for Jim the promoter. After a few minutes Andrew looks at his watch and tells Silver he had better get on his toes as the show is about to end. Silver finishes his tea and walks back stage to await the end of the show and to get the lads out of there in a hurry. Silver instructs the other minders to just form a guard around the lads and to push their way through the crowd and not to stop for anything. Jim walks back stage and tells Silver the bus is sitting outside and is ready to whisk the boys back to the hotel. After the group does its encore the boys run back stage and the sweat is running out of Mick as Silver instructs them on how to get out with little bother. Jim says it would be better if they went out the back door tonight. The bus would be sitting there for the roadies and stage hands but they are going to go in the bus out front.

"Let's call it a little decoy. So Paddy, you and the rest of the boys lead them out the back door and straight to the bus and straight to the hotel. No stops along the road. We have to do this all again tomorrow night. So it will probably be more straight forward."

Silver tells the group he would lead and the other guys would form a wall around them and straight onto the bus and away we go. All was going like clockwork as they ran down the entry behind the cinema when two big guys jumped out in front of Silver and tells him that they hated all this devils music and they better not come back again. Silver pushes one of the guys out of his way, while the other throws a Judas punch at him. Silver tells the group and the minders to get on the bus. He will follow them in two minutes, as he wrestles with the two men. After Silver gathers himself and throws two punches and knocks the two men down, he then grabs one and asks him, "Who sent you here?"

"Nobody," the big guy answers. As Silver draws back to punch him again he yells, "don't hit me again. It was Harry Robinson."

"Why," asks Silver, "why is he interested in this?"

"He wants the show to fail." Silver hits the guy a punch on the side of the head and calls him a yellow livered waster. Silver then runs and gets on the bus and the driver takes off just as the fans rumble that they have been duped. The bus drives up the Grosvenor Road and up on to the Falls Road and heads straight for the Woodbourne Hotel. On arrival at the hotel, Silver leads the stones off the bus and as they enter all the staff are standing waiting to see them. Patsy Finnegan, Roy Smyth, Sean Dillon, Joe McGrath, Tom and Mickey McCauley, Noel Gorman, John Little, Leana and a few of the guests are waiting in anticipation for the biggest thing ever to happen in the hotel. Just then big Des Davison appears and the staff disperse as The Stones run up the stairs to their respective rooms. Silver then grabs a chair and calls a waiter and orders a bottle of stout and a large whiskey.

* * *

The next day Silver is up early and is having breakfast in the restaurant when Jim walks over to him and sits down. "That was a good job last night but what was the fisticuffs about?"

"Well, two guys tried to scare me off; first of all with the religion thing, and then after I banged one of them, a few times he told me that Harry Robinson was trying to put the kybosh on tomorrow night's show by scaring the group."

"What in the hell are you talking about Paddy?"

"I'm just telling you what he said but as far as I'm concerned it's not a big problem. I'll deal with it."

"I don't want any hassle. Who is this person Paddy, whatever his name is?"

"Look, I will deal with it."

"But I don't want you to deal with it; I don't want anything to happen. I don't want any trouble."

"Jim, you employed me to look after things. Now what do you want to do? Do you want to do it yourself because it's no skin off my nose?"

"I only wish it was Sunday. Them boys would be on the plane and I would be able to relax. Now listen to me Paddy. Please, no trouble, do the job and for fuck sake, keep your hands in your pockets."

"Jim you're the boss but if anybody lifts their hands to me and I mean anybody I will knock them out and that includes you."

"Now don't be getting angry. I was told you'd be trouble and it sounds like they were right." Silver is now getting annoyed with Jim.

"Listen Mister I didn't start the trouble, but I'll tell you one thing, I usually end it one way or the other."

"Look Paddy, I didn't mean to be talking to you that way. My nerves are wrecked. This is my first big promotion and it's doing my head in."

"Okay Jim. Let me do my job, one way or the other, and you do yours, and Bob's your uncle."

"All I want you to do, is to do exactly the same tonight without the fighting and I will be happy and don't forget to bring your gear with you on the bus so when you get the group on the bus you can head on home."

"Great Jim. What time are we leaving at?"

"About half six in case there's a hitch. You never know. My motto is it's better being a half an hour early than a half hour late. That makes sense. So when the boys come down, just keep an eye on them and keep them out of trouble. There's two big weddings here today and I don't want the boys messing about. They're always up to stupid pranks as far as I know. Their manager Andrew told me they love having a laugh."

"I met him. He's a funny wee guy but seems levelheaded enough," says Silver. As the day goes on one wedding party arrives and Silver is out looking at the bride and groom who arrive in two identical Aston Martin DB5s with similar registration numbers. Silver had never seen anything like it before. These were things beyond him and his peers. It was sheer opulence on par with nothing Silver had ever seen. Champagne on arrival for the guests and a free bar. This was some wedding. A second wedding arrives about an hour later but it was a smaller affair and Silver knows a couple of the guests. After a while Mick Jagger and the rest of the lads appear down in the main hall of the hotel and before long become the focus of attention from both wedding parties. One man comes over to Silver and asks him could he do him a favour.

"What would that be, Mickey?" asks Silver.

"My daughter who's the bride would love a photograph with a couple of The Stones if you can arrange it. There's a score in it for you."

"When are you doing the pictures?" asks Silver.

"In a few minutes. We're going out to the garden and it would make for great memories if you could get two of the group to get a picture taken with the wedding party."

"Leave it with me."

"Do you want the score now Silver?"

"No, when the job is done you can pay me."

A while later the wedding party is standing on the front lawn of the Woodbourne getting photographs taken when out walks Silver followed by the group and they all join in with the wedding party. The bride and the groom and the guests are over the moon. Mickey follows Silver across the lawn after the photographs and slips him a twenty-pound note which Silver discreetly spits on and puts it in his pocket.

"I could make a good wee business out of this," says Silver. Mickey and him both laugh.

Later that night Silver is walking through the lounge with his case and he walks out and puts it on the bus. As he is walking back, Des the manager calls him and tells him that he has an outstanding bill for nine pounds for drinks and cigarettes. "I was told that I could order anything I wanted and Mister Benner would pay for it."

"Well he left no word of that here. So I'm afraid you will have to pay the outstanding bill Sir. Silver hands him the twenty pound note and says, "Easy come, easy go. It didn't even get time to warm up in my pocket."

"What do you mean Sir?"

"Oh you wouldn't understand. Just bring me my change and I will be on my way." Des brings him his change and thanks him for his staying in the hotel and hopes that he may meet him again. Silver looks at him and laughs, "at these prices I don't think so, but thanks for the courtesy. I don't think I will be back. It just wouldn't suit my pocket." As Silver is standing in the hall waiting for the group to come down the stairs, Mick Jagger appears in a white outfit followed by the rest of the group and they are parading up and down the hall lounge all to the amazement of the customers and staff. It's as if he is giving an impromptu performance without the singing. Under closer scrutiny it's nerves and they can't wait to get on the bus and get the job done. Two minutes later everyone is one the bus heading for the Ritz Cinema and Silver is telling the boys to just do as they done last night and everything will be okay. He also tells them that this is his last night and he loved every minute working with them. The group all stand up and clap Silver and Mick gives a wee singalong of It's all over now. Suddenly they are outside the cinema and Silver gets off the bus, calls the other minders who are standing among a now high-spirited crowd and tells them to do the same as last night. No stopping and just form a wall around the boys. Silver gets back on the bus and asks the boys are they ready and they charge off the bus and straight up the steps leading to the entrance to the cinema. After getting the group in safely Silver decides to go for a drink of tea in the Rotunda where he meets Andrew again who is sitting sipping a coffee. Silver joins him and they get into deep conversation. Andrew asks him would he like to go for a drink after the show.

"Surely," says Silver, "we can go over to the Washington Bar across the street, but it closes at ten so they will have to be sharpish after the band finishes." About two hours later the show is over and they use that back door tactic to elude the now thousands of fans that have arrived from all over Belfast, lining the streets. So all the group go out the back door and onto the bus and as Silver gets everyone settled, he bids them farewell. As he gets off the bus he is suddenly surrounded by thousands of screaming fans. After a few minutes and with the help of Silver, the bus takes off and The Rolling Stones are gone. Silver walks back into the cinema looking for Andrew. A roadie tells him that he's outside the front door, waiting on him. As Silver is walking through the main hall he meets Jim, who hands him an envelope with his wages in it.

"I won't need you again Paddy. I think trouble follows you and I don't want it, but thanks for helping me out."

"Let me tell you something Jim, I don't really understand you people. Do you use everyone in a similar fashion or am I imagining it?"

"It's simple. I don't need people like you; I want my promotions to be fight free with no trouble."

"The only way I can answer that Jim, is that you're looking a magician and that I am not. But you'll come looking again, I can assure you of that." Silver puts the envelope in his pocket and walks out to the front door and sees Andrew waiting on him. He's wearing a brown velvet coat and corduroy trousers and a multi coloured shirt and blue tinted glasses. Silver ponders for a minute as to whether he wants to go for a drink with Andrew but being a man of his word he walks over and the pair walk down May Street towards the Washington bar. As they reach the front of the bar the sound of the roller shutter comes down and Silver shouts in that he is outside at the door. After a few minutes Silver kicks the shutter and Andrew asks, "Where now?" Silver asks him where he is staying and Andrew tells him that he's staying in the International Hotel but he doesn't recollect where it actually is.

"Follow me," says Silver, "it's at the bottom of the street and a pal of mine owns it. I'd forgotten where you were staying." As they are walking into the hotel a porter asks are they guests and for there room number. Silver just pushes on by the porter and after a few minutes Andrew follows. As they head to the bar Silver pulls out the envelope and opens it and orders a drink. Silver counts the money and there is only forty quid in the envelope and he tells Andrew that Jim stroked him on a tenner.

"Don't worry. I will reimburse you and charge him it in my expenses. He shouldn't have done that. You looked after the boys well." After a few hours both men are very drunk and Andrew tells Silver he would like to see where he lives and it would be fun to see the town. Silver tells him that he literally only lives around the corner and it's a bit late for wandering about the town. But Andrew insists and after another couple of drinks the two men head for Silver's house in the market. When they arrive at the front door Mary, who had heard them singing coming down the street meets them at the front door.

"You're in a terrible state. I thought you where going to give the drink a miss for a while.

And who is this crater you have with you?"

"This Mary is my friend, Andrew Loog Oldham."

"Where did you get a name like that son? You can be sure of one thing. He definitely wasn't born in the Market. Come on in before the neighbours come out to nosey." Silver and Andrew walk in to the kitchen and Silver points to his chair and tells Andrew to sit down and he asks Mary to put the tea on and make a couple of sandwiches. Andrew is amazed by the size of the kitchen and asks Silver all about the house and how many bedrooms it has.

"It's your typical two up and two down and a wee scullery down the back and an outside toilet."

"You mean you have to go outside to use the lavatory?"

"Yes. Why is there anything wrong with that? asks Silver. Mary arrives with two cups of tea and a couple of ham sandwiches on a small plate. Silver grabs one and hands the plate to Andrew and Mary announces that she is going to bed and would they mind keeping the noise down. She doesn't want the child wakened. Mary makes her way to bed and after a few minutes Silver and Andrew are fast asleep on the chairs.

The next morning, Silver is awakened by the sound of someone knocking noisily on the front door. As Silver gathers himself up and walks to the door, he opens it and is met by Jim.

"Look Paddy. Have you seen the boys manager. You were the last one seen with him and his plane leaves in about an hour and he can't be found."

Silver laughs. "Now I told you that you would come back looking my help and another thing you stole a tenner on me."

"I didn't steal a tenner on you. That was to pay for the drink in the hotel."

"I already paid for it. In fact it was nine quid so if you want my help to find the man your looking for I need wages. Jim pulls a bundle of money out of his pocket and hands Silver thirty pounds. Silver looks at it and then Jim hands him another twenty.

"If you find him, I'll be eternally grateful."

"That's a horse with a different tail. Last night I was a troublemaker and finished. Funny how things can change in a day."

"Look Paddy. Get ready. We have to find this man or it won't look good for me."

"Come on in till I get ready and I have someone I'd like you to meet." Jim follows Silver into the kitchen and there is Andrew fast asleep on the chair.

"Is that the man you're looking for?"

"You're not so slow Paddy. Anybody thinks that they're going to meet a mug, may take one with them, when they are going to meet you. Here give me a hand to get him sorted. Have you any coffee in the house?"

"Coffee? Where do you think you are, in Buckingham palace? This is the Market. Nobody drinks coffee around here; it's tea Jim, good old-fashioned Lyons green label tea." After a few minutes they get Andrew wakened and get a cup of sweet tea into him and out into Jim's car. As they get Andrew into the back seat he lies down and says to Silver, "It was a pleasure meeting you Sir, a fucking pleasure." Jim looks at Silver, gets into the car and as he drives off he thanks Silver and says "Maybe you can work for me again." Jim laughs as he drives off.

Chapter 14

After weeks of no work, Mary asks Silver would he not go out and look for a proper nine to five job. "I've never had a job like that in my life and I don't think I could handle it. When I worked in the gas works in Lisburn it near killed me."

"No education, that's what's wrong with you. If you had went to school when you were young instead of running around the markets thinking you where a cattle dealer at twelve years of age, things may have been different."

"Look woman, don't be preaching to me. Do you not think things are bad enough; I have hardly the price of a pint these days."

"Do you ever think that sometimes we don't have the price of the dinner in this house? If it weren't for my mother we would probably have starved." Silver gets up and grabs his coat and tells Mary that he's heard enough and he's going for a walk into town. On his way through the town he meets a couple of old friends and stops to have a yarn with them. Then as he is walking down Castle Street he bumps into Harry Robinson who calls him aside.

"Look Paddy. If you come to court on the sixteenth I will have an envelope for you that will have a right few quid in it. All you have to do, is agree with my barrister and everything will go well. Big Billy and me have worked out our differences and we'll just say let bygones be bygones."

"That sounds okay, but can I have a sub from that envelope now. Things are bad. I will do as you say. That's a promise come court day."

Harry reaches into his pocket and pulls out a ten-pound note and hands it to Silver. "There's two hundred quid for you on the morning of the court. It will get you over Christmas and everybody will be happy as Larry."

"Who's Larry?" asks Silver?

"Nobody knows whom Larry is. It's just one of them stupid sayings but the two hundred will make you and the wife and kid happy won't it."

Yes it would. I need a bit of good luck because I've had nothing but bad luck and I'm sick sore and tired of it."

"Where you off to now?" asks Harry.

'I'm going up the Falls Road to see a friend of mine and get a few drinks and then head home."

"Okay, now remember be at the court, sharp on the sixteenth and be clean and tidy as the judge will be looking at you and you don't want to look like a corner boy do you?"

"I'm away on here because I'm sick and tired of people lecturing me. It's becoming boring."

Silver and Harry bid each other good luck and Silver walks off up Castle Street and on up to the Pound Loney. He has a drink in the Arkle Inn but the person he is looking for isn't there. So he heads around to Milford Street and walks into a big pub at the corner of Cinnamon Street and orders a pint. There are only two people in it; Bill Jack and a wee musician from east Belfast who most of the customers only knew as Sammy. As Silver and Bill Jack have a bit of banter across the bar to one another, Silver then asks the barman if Lily McCormack has been in.

The bar man replies that wee Sammy was also waiting on her. As the time passes and Silver consumes a lot more drink he asks wee Sammy what his business is with Lily. Sammy replies that he is going out with her and they are going into the town for a drink when she arrives. Silver for some reason or another gets agitated and starts to get a bit angry towards Sammy. Bill Jack butts in and tells Silver that wee Sammy is okay and to leave him alone. Silver gets another few whiskeys and then he asks Bill Jack what business of his was it how he spoke to Sammy. The barman then interrupts both men and warns them to be quiet or he will ask them to leave. Silver gets a bit abrupt with the barman and Bill Jack asks Silver to be quiet and to finish his drink.

"You're one of them Hawks from across the other side of the Falls aren't you. Well nobody tells me what to do, so mind your own business." Silver pushes wee Sammy in a sort of boisterous playful way and knocks him of his stool. Bill Jack thinking Silver done it for badness attacks him. The barman comes from behind the bar and manages to push Silver out the front door and then tells Bill Jack to leave. As Bill Jack is walking out the front door Silver is standing with his coat off and calling for Bill Jack to have a fair go. Bill Jack takes off his coat and both square up to one another. By this time a large crowd has gathered and formed a ring and the two men go toe to toe. After a few punches are thrown Silver connects to Bill Jack's jaw and he slips and falls but someone in the crowd helps him quickly back to his feet and pushes him towards Silver and the two men wrestle for a few minutes and Bill connects to Silver's jaw and Silver falls. Bill Jack is just about to punch him again when somebody shouts, "Cops! Cops! Here's the cops! Bill Jack grabs his coat and takes off down Cinnamon Street and into his own home and Silver is left standing in the street while the crowd disperses. Two policemen walk over to Silver and ask what the commotion is all about.

"I had a few drinks too many Sir and I fell and somebody gave me hand and got me back on my feet."

"Where are you from Sir?" asks one of the policemen.

"I'm from the Market area and I'm heading home right now. I've had enough of all this drink."

"So you weren't fighting then Silver?"

"No I'm half drunk and I'm heading home right now to see the wife and the wee one."

"Well, we will escort you down on to Divis Street and see you on your way. But if you think we believe you, your barking up the wrong street, we know all about you. Silver McKee the big hard man. Look at the state of you, you should be ashamed of yourself. As Silver is walking home the words of the cop echoed in his ears: 'you should be ashamed of yourself. Silver McKee the big hard man!' About a half an hour later Silver arrives home and walks into his kitchen and Mary takes one look at him.

"Paddy I can't take much more of this."

"You know something Mary, neither can I."

* * *

Silver has now fallen from grace and has taken to the drink and lost all self dignity and it's only by the grace of God that Mary has stayed. As Silver stumbles in on another drunken night Mary is at her wits end and tells him it's time for him to choose. Either he quits the drink, or Anne and her are going to live in her mothers. The next night followed a now familiar pattern of Silver coming home drunk and sleeping on the chair and he's got to the stage that he can't even eat and the weight is falling off him. The next day Silver is leaving the house and Mary looks at him.

"Paddy, I loved you from the day and hour I met you. But I'm tired. Look at me I've aged twenty years in two years. I look like an old woman. I haven't had a new outfit in years and the child isn't much better. What's going to become of us?"

"Give my head peace, woman. All I hear is people preaching to me. Between you and Barney Ross telling me to get off the drink, I'm about fed up with it all." Silver heads out and is walking around the Market when he is stopped by a young guy about twenty years of age and he tells Silver that he's finished as a hard man. He's a drunk and if he ever lifts his hand to his Da again he'll beat the fuck out of him.

"Who's your Da?"

"Johnny Burke, that's who."

"Well if I hit your Da he deserved it." The young guy gets stuck into Silver, who hasn't even sobered up at that stage and punches the face off him until a few men appear and separate the fight. Silver just pushes everyone away and shouts leave me alone and let me get on with my life. Silver then makes his way around to the Black Bull and when he walks in the bar goes silent.

"A bottle of stout and a whiskey, Tommy," says Silver to the barman.

"Look Paddy, it's none of my business but is it not time you where catching yourself on?"

"I come out of the house to get my head showered and I get the same in the bar. Tommy, you stick your drink up your arse. I'm away to a good pub and I'll never be back here." Ten minutes later and Silver is in Mooney's, a large pub right in the middle of Belfast. As he orders a drink a solicitor friend comes in and joins him for a drink.

"Jesus Silver, you're in some state. What have you being doing with your self?"

"Now don't you start Mark. I'm about up to here..." Silver points to his neck, "...with good advice. I haven't been the same since I got shot in London."

"I never heard about that. You mean you got shot with a real gun."

"Well, its wasn't a pellet gun. Luckily it went straight through me leg."

"Well, I hope you got a few pounds compensation?"

"No, but as soon as I was able to travel, I got out of that God forsaken place."

"Was it the cops that shot you?"

"No it was a gangster. A real gangster fired at a crowd and I got it and it has fucked me, pardon the language."

"Look, I've to go back to court. Why don't you come around to my office someday next week and I will see if your entitled to compensation."

"Mark, if I bought a duck it would probably drown. No, let me rephrase that, it would drown." Silver gets drunk and is heading home when a group of young lads who are following him start slagging and calling him names. One of the group comes forward and asks him for a fag and Silver reaches into his pocket to give him a cigarette when he suddenly hits Silver a punch on the face. Within minutes Silver is on the ground being kicked about like a rag doll as he rolls about trying to protect himself. The kicks are flying into his stomach and his ribs. He covers up his head and the kicking continues for a few minutes until a young guy appears and throws the youths off Silver. It's Fra Ward and as he lifts Silver he realises it's his idol and sets him against a window frame and tries to sort him out. Silver looks at him and realises it's the kid who travelled with him from the Puck Fair and looked after him on the Heysham boat.

"So this is what you want to be son. This is the worst period of my life Fra.

People I could have beaten off me, like swatting flies off a cow, are attacking me. Look at me. I'm finished. I'm a beaten man, all washed up."

"Let me walk you home in case some other idiots get the same idea about having a fight with the great Silver McKee and making a name for themselves." As Fra gets near to Silver's house he tells him of a mate of his called Goldie Donoghue who runs a wee boxing club and he may look after him and get him fit again so he can carry his head high without someone attacking him every time he's in a pub. Fra knocks on Silver's door but there's no reply. But Silver has a key and he opens the door under pressure and Fra walks him into the kitchen and sets him on a chair. Fra has a look around him and a tear come to his eyes at the squalor his hero is now living in. As Fra is walking out he tells Silver to go up the Falls and says: "Tell Goldie that I told you to go to the club and I guarantee you he will help you. He'll do it for me no sweat; I will have a word with him and sort it out." Fra is walking up home to the Falls and he can't get Silver out of his mind. As he is walking past a billboard he punches it and makes a large hole in it then runs off in a state of panic. His hero is gone; his whole life has been built around eclipsing Silver and taking over his mantle and now this.

The next morning Silver awakens on the chair and he can't move. His ribs and stomach are covered in black and blue marks and he cannot get up on his feet. He tries to remember what happened the day and night before but all he remembers is Fra taking him home and those words he uttered, 'Goldie Donoghue will look after you and get you fit.'

Later on that day Croaky knocks on the door and Silver struggles to get up and open the door to let him in.

"Jesus Christ! In the name of God, what has been happening here? This is like a pigsty. When are you going to catch yourself on Paddy? You're a fucking disgrace."

"Look Croaky, for this last month or so all I have been listening to is advice: some of it good; some of it bad and I really don't need any more. I know your heart is in the right place but give me a break, I'm a sick man and I know what to do."

"It's not about knowing what to do, it's about doing something about it." Croaky puts his hand in his pocket and gives Silver a couple of pounds and tells him to get himself something to eat or he's going to starve to death. Silver reluctantly takes the money and as usual spits on the notes and puts them in his pocket and thanks Croaky and reminds him that he hasn't forgotten him. Croaky tells him that if things change for him, he won't forget him. He has to go back to work but will call in every morning to see if he's okay.

"You mean you will call in to see if I'm still alive." Both laugh.

"And for God's sake get some woman from around here to come in and clean this place up. It reminds me of Allams, the smell is terrible." Croaky walks to the door and as he is walking out he says to Silver, "the good old days are over Paddy, and anything we get now, we have to work for."

"I'm in no fit state to work since I got shot. My leg is giving me jip."

"If I had the air to that I could sing it. Give it a rest, get up and get on with it. Next case." Croaky walks out and Silver gets himself up off the chair and goes to the scullery and washes his face. He then grabs his coat and makes his way out to the street. Young Michael Ross is driving down the street in his wee van and Silver waves him down.

"Hello Paddy, how's it going? Where you off to?"

"I need a lift up the Shankill. I'm going for a drink. Do you want to join me? I have a couple of quid enough for the two of us."

"I'm your man. Jump in." Silver struggles around the car and with great difficulty climbs into the passenger seat and off they go. "What's wrong with you Paddy, you don't look too clever?"

"I got a bit of a beating up the street yesterday. Some young buck said I hit his Da years ago."

"And what did you do?"

"I couldn't do anything. I was half drunk for a start. I'm really not doing well."

"Was he from around here, the Market?"

"Yes. I forget his name but he gave me a tanking. Luckily enough, a few men that know me separated it."

"Fuck me! I don't believe it. I could beat most of the young lads knocking about and he beat you. I can't believe it."

"I also got attacked in the town last night. Young Ward from up the Falls Road was right there. It would be a lot of young guys out to make a name for themselves and be able to say 'I done Silver.'"

"No chance, Paddy! No chance! Get your act together and you'll be back to what you were."

"I can't see it son."

"Look, I'm going to be straight with you. You're not only letting yourself down your letting your people down, the people from the Market who always looked up to you. " Michael stops the van. "I don't know whether to go for a drink with you or not. I'm worried for you Paddy. I'm serious. You're a good man."

"Look, this is my last go at it. I need a drink so I can sleep now. Drive the van up to the Rex Bar and we will have a few. I want to see a friend of mine. Stormy."

"Are you going to fight him?"

"I might have to. You see he was slabbering about me or was that bookie Quinn just mouthing off?"

"Look Paddy, the state your in. I would beat you in a fair fight, so Stormy would hurt you and I mean bad."

"We'll see about that but I need to get it out of my system. It's doing my head in."

"Do you think that's why you're drinking so much Paddy? Are you afraid of him?"

"Never feared any man in my life and I don't fear Stormy Weatherall. Here we are park the van up somewhere. I don't want you drinking and driving. It will be all right I'll only have one and that will do me but you can have as many as you like."

Silver and Michael both walk into the bar and as Silver walks to the bar the barman comes from behind the bar and tells Silver he is barred.

"Look, I only want a couple of drinks while I'm waiting on Stormy. I've to meet him here when he finishes work."

"Has Stormy agreed to meet you here?"

"Yes, I've to give him a message then I will be on my way."

"Well, while your waiting on him you can have a couple of drinks but then you will have to go, and another thing keep your hands in your pockets."

"You can forget that last remark."

"By the looks of you, you don't need to bother. You're an old done man, finished. If Stormy blew on you, you'd fall."

"Okay, less of the sermon. Give me a bottle of stout and a halfun of whiskey and give the young lad a bottle of lager."

"Go over there and sit in the corner. I'll bring it over to you." The barman brings the drink over and sets it on the table and looks at Silver. "I've never seen anyone go down hill as much in such a short time. What have you done to yourself?"

"I fell over some straw and a hen kicked me." Silver and Michael laugh.

"It must have been some hen you fool," says the barman. After another few drinks the door opens and in walks Stormy still wearing his white boiler suit that he wears in the flourmill. Stormy orders a pint of Guinness and the barman points to the corner where Silver is sitting.

"Who is it?" asks Stormy.

"It's your old adversary McKee."

"That's not him," says Stormy, "Oh, it's him all right."

"I wasn't going to serve him but he said he had a message to give you, and as soon as he gives you it, he's going out. He's become a bit of a nuisance." Stormy takes a drink from his pint and walks over to Silver and sits down.

"So what's the message you have for me Paddy?"

"Firstly Connolly Quinn said that he's going to get you to sort me out. Any truth in that?

"Look Paddy, I've only finished work, I'm tired and I'm in no mood to listen to nonsense." Silver tries to stand up to remonstrate with Stormy. "If you weren't in such a bad way I'd break your jaw. Now I think its time you left and in a hurry before I change my mind."

Silver throws a right hand as Michael gets up and tries to intervene but its too late. Stormy knocks Silver to the ground. The barman rushes over and shouts "That's it, out you go you're a troublemaker."

"I'll get him out. He's drunk. Leave him alone. You wouldn't have done that a year or two ago," says Michael.

"It doesn't matter what I could or couldn't do a year ago. It's today that counts and he's finished, and I'm sorry to see it. I thought we where friends now but I was wrong. Both of you get out before I start." The barman helps Michael get Silver to his feet and rushes both of them through the front door. As the barman walks back behind the bar he says to Stormy, "that man's a real nuisance."

"That man was the hardest man I ever met, and he was a gentleman. But that's what drink does to people. Set me up a pint and a whiskey my head is spinning, and I've just lost a good old pal, and it's a pity."

Meanwhile Michael is trying to get Silver into the van and he is having none of it. After a few minutes Michael is getting fed up and he shouts at Silver.

"Every time I look at you I could cry. You're a wreck of a man now. Get into the van before I drive off and leave you."

Next day Silver awakens in his usual place, the armchair in the kitchen but things are different. The house is wrecked and he wonders who done this to his home. After a cup of tea and a couple of aspirin he starts to have flashbacks and he then realises it was himself who done the damage. He had taken his resentment for Stormy out on his own home and he knows it's over for him unless there's a miracle in his now twisted life. The name Goldie Donohue kept ringing in his head and he tries to remember what it meant to him and why he was thinking of the name so much. He decides to go for a walk down into the town and see if he can get the price of a drink. As he is walking through Royal Avenue he bumps into a group of young fellows and one of them is Fra Ward. Fra stops to talk to Silver and suddenly it all comes back to him.

"Would you do me a favour son?"

"If it's the price of a drink your looking the answer is no, but I will buy you your breakfast in the ITL café."

Silver looks at Fra and replies, "do you know something son, I've had my last drink and that is final. What I want you to do is to take me up to see Goldie or whatever his name is. I want to get fit and I'm game to give it a try."

"I'll tell you better, Silver I will take you up and I will train you myself. Goldie won't mind and I'm not working so what do you say to that."

"I'm your man. When shall we go to his gym?"

"No time like the present. Fra tells his friends that he has to go a message with Silver and he will meet them later at the corner. Silver and Fra walk off down Royal Avenue and head up the Falls Road to Goldie's gym. As they walk in Fra calls Goldie aside and explains what he wants to do and Goldie agrees but tells Fra that he thinks he's wasting his time.

"Take that corner and stay out of the way of the boxers and it will be all right, but no interference with the fighters." Fra walks over to a heavy punch bag and asks Silver to hit it as hard as he can. Silver looks at him in dismay but throws a punch at the bag and Fra swings it out of his way. Silver misses and Fra laughs, "You see, that's what's wrong. If that was a real person they would have you knocked cold." Fra tells Silver to go home get a good sleep and he will meet him here at ten o'clock the morrow morning. "Bring a clean vest and some light footwear. I will get you a pair of pants, but don't let me down."

Silver looks at Fra and says to him; "You're serious about this Fra aren't you. I can't understand. Why do you want to do this for me?"

"Look Silver, I'm doing it for myself and you want to know the reason why?"

"Don't keep me in suspense," says Silver cheekily.

"I don't want to finish up like you. I told you that you where my idol and I wanted to emulate you, but look at you. Who would want you as a role model?"

Silver scratches his head and is a little confused. "Look be here tomorrow morning as planned and I will try and make you the man you always where." Silver puts his hand out and Fra shakes it.

"You have a deal," says Silver. Silver tells Fra he's going home for a kip and to tidy the house up. He will be back up to the club in the morning. Silver walks out the door of the club and Goldie calls Fra over.

"Who's that oul idiot Fra?"

"That Goldie was the hardest man ever to wear shoe leather in Ireland."
Goldie laughs.

"Next you're going to tell me that was Silver McKee."

"You got it in one my friend."

"What! That wee man is Silver. I don't believe it and if it is, he's in a shocking state. I would be worried about training him; you're liable to kill him. You let him take it very easy Fra and don't be rushing him. Get his muscle built up a bit and get him half fit and if it is Silver the rest will follow because he could punch like Rocky Marciano and maybe even harder."

Fra throws a right hand at a punchbag and turns to Goldie, "You mean like that."

Goldie laughs, "Well something like that."

"Goldie if you could just watch from the distance and keep me right. If I'm pushing him too hard or anything else. I want to do this myself but I do want your help in the background. I want to see that man back to his glory days; I can see him in his minds eye walking around the Belfast horse fair with his yellow Crombie, his buffers knot, and his yellow boots. He was like a film star with his ash plant in one hand, and a cigarette in the other, a sight to behold as he strode around the markets square. Ever since I first saw him I said to myself, I want to be like him, and I will. Mark my words Goldie."

"Look Fra, I've known you since you where a child and all your family. The best advice I can give you is, be yourself. Don't try to live your life as an image of someone else, live it to the full but in your own image."

"Okay Goldie. I will see you in the morning and I hope he comes up and most of all he quits the drink. It's killing him slowly but surely."

"We'll keep that in mind and you will be all right, but remember everything is alright in moderation, even some poison. "

The next day Fra is shadow boxing in the club and looking at the clock every few minutes. It's now a quarter to eleven and Silver was to be here at ten thirty so he is getting a bit worried. He calls Goldie and tells him that he may have been right and he's wasting his time, so he's going to leave at eleven o'clock and if Silver calls he can tell him he's not interested anymore in helping him. Goldie tells him to be patient and at least give him a few minutes and then he can leave knowing he tried his best. Fra looks at the clock its now eleven o'clock and he tells Goldie he is definitely going and he isn't staying any longer.

Just at that the door opens and Silver looks around. Silver puts his head in the door and sheepishly calls out for Fra. Fra's face lights up and he walks over to Silver and tells him laughingly that's he's late. Silver tells him that he couldn't find the place and some kid showed him the way.

"The changing room is over there," says Goldie, pointing to a very small room. Just throw your gear on the bench it will be alright. There's no one else coming in today." Silver walks over to the changing room and strips and Fra throws him in a pair of shorts.

"When your ready we will start and we're going to take it easy for the first week. After that we double up and so on. Goldie is going to keep an eye on the sidelines and if he sees anything I don't, he will tell us both." Silver walks out into the gym and Fra looks at the man he admired and wonders what was it all about. He is only half the man he was when he saw him at the Puck Fair and he has lost a lot of weight. Fra looks at him and tells him he looks like he needs a good feed. He asks Silver to just throw a few punches at the heavy bag but not that hard, just loosen up for ten minutes. Silver starts throwing punches at the punch bag and after a few minutes he is totally out of breath. He has to sit down as the sweat runs down his brow and he looks at Fra and asks, "do you think I can get back to what I was?"

"We'll never know until we try, but it's normal for you to feel like this. You have been abusing your body for a long time so it needs nurturing and time." Silver gets up and starts punching again and he gets carried away and goes into a frenzy and is hitting the bag so hard it is swinging so hard Fra has to stop him. "You have to control your anger Paddy because if you don't you will run out of steam very quick. As I said, just take it easy." After about an hour they call it quits and arrange for Silver to come back the next day. "You will be very sore tomorrow but I want you to come up and continue and after a week or so you won't feel a thing. You can bet on it." Silver goes and gets changed and Fra tells him he will walk him down a little when he gets ready. Goldie calls Fra and tells him to slow it down from tomorrow, as he doesn't want a dead man in the club. Fra and Silver are walking down the road and Fra is continuously asking Silver about who he fought and how does he feel being assaulted by a couple of young guys.

"Look Fra, when you get the name of being a hard man there is always some one waiting to challenge you and some wait until your old or knackered. To me that's part of it all, but let me tell you something, I never called myself a hard man and I never bullied anyone, and I have to live with it whether I like it or not. So before you start styling yourself on someone like me ask yourself do you want all that hassle?"

"But I am young Paddy, I'm only twenty-one. I have a long time to go before I'm old."

"I thought that too,but as an old pal of mine said it's like the blink of an eye and looking back he's one hundred percent right."

"I'm going into Victor's ice cream shop for a smokie. Would you like to come in for one," asks Fra.

"An ice cream shop, are you joking? Next you will be asking me if I'm going to become a priest." Both laugh as they walk into Victors and Fra orders two Smokies. As they sit in the box eating their Smokies, Silver tells Fra that he nearly got jailed the last time he was up this way. "I had a drink next door in the Arkle Inn and then went around to the Pound Loney and got into a fight with a good guy called Bill Jack. I was drunk and I should have been minding my own business." Both finish their ice cream and head out and are walking down Castle Street when Silver spies Connolly Quinn standing outside a bookmakers shop.

"I'm going to kill him. Stay here Fra. I'm going over to pull the head of that fucker Quinn." Fra grabs him by the lapels and remonstrates with him; if you go over and pull him we're finished. As they are both arguing Quinn sees them and slips away down Chapel Lane and Fra tells Silver he's gone.

"There'll be plenty of time for the Quinn's of this world but until you gather yourself together you couldn't beat Casey's drum." Fra and Silver bid each other good luck and Fra tells him, "no drink and I will see you in the morning."

* * *

After a few weeks training Silver is starting to look a bit like the man he was three or four years previous. He's bursting to get revenge on some of the people that have messed him about.

"Another fortnight and you will be as fit as a fiddle Paddy. Then it's up to yourself after that. You will be able to walk through the town like years ago, when you where the man, and no one could touch you."

Chapter 15

S ome time later after Silver has sorted himself out, he recognizes that it's time to try and get Mary and the child back. He has had the house tided up and got a friend to wallpaper it and give it a lick of paint. He is worried that he has left it too long and Mary might be happy to stay on her own. He knows that he is a different person now but will have to prove to Mary that he is serious about quitting the drink and behaving himself. After sitting with his thoughts, he decides to walk around to Barney Ross's yard and try and get young Michael to drive him up to his mother in law's house. As he walks into Ross's yard Barney sees him and walks over to him and shakes his hand.

"I never thought I would see the day. You're a new man Paddy. What can I do for you?"

"I need someone to run me up to my mother-in-law's and I thought your young Michael would do it. I don't want him to do it for nothing. I will give him a couple of pound for petrol."

"He's out doing a bit of hawking but I will run you up myself. Let me get the car keys and my coat." Barney and Silver are on their way up to the in-laws' house and as they are driving up the lane Silver asks Barney, "Would you put in a good word for me to Mary. I know I've let her down a few times but it's different now."

"Do you think I would have driven you up here if I didn't think you'd changed. I think Mary will take one look at you and she will know for herself that you are clean and sober."

"I don't want you to tell lies Barney. I just want you to back me up."

"I wouldn't be telling any lies. For you anyway, so don't even ask." As the car pulls up outside the front door Mary appears with Anne in her arms. As Silver is standing talking to Mary, Barney starts the car up and Silver walks over to him and tells him he will only be a few minutes. "You can have all the time you want. I think it would be better if I leave. You can always get a taxi for you, Mary and the child."

"But what if she doesn't want to come home? What am I supposed to do?"

"Let me tell you, a wee bird told me that she's ready to go home, so spend a bit of time with her then take them both home. Better still I will call back in an hour. How's that sound. Hopefully I will be taking youse all home." Barney winks at Silver.

"You seem to know more about my life than me."

"Yes maybe I do, but remember I haven't been drinking day and night but you have." Barney drives off to the amazement of Silver who looks at Mary and she just smiles. Mary invites him into her mother's house and they are sitting talking when her mother walks in.

"Look what the wind blew in. Did you forget you had a wife and child?"

"Mother, can't you see he's changed. Look he's clean and tidy and off the drink."

"Yes, but for how long?"

"Only for today missus, only for today, but I'm trying." Mary gets up and a few minutes later returns with a small suitcase and some clothing over her arm. Silver is nursing Anne who is bawling her head off at this strange man whose holding her in his arms. After Mary packs her case she explains to her mother that she is going back home but will call up in a few days to see how she's keeping. Mary's mother is very displeased looking, and tells Mary that she is making a big mistake, but she will keep her room ready, as she doesn't think she will be away that long. A few minutes of silence and Mary has now got Anne in her arms. They hear the sound of a car horn and Silver gets up and goes to the window and looks outside.

"It's Barney. It's time to go. Here, let me carry that case Mary. You can carry the child."

"Let me carry the case?" says Mary, "... that's the first time I ever heard you offer to do anything where there wasn't something for you in it, Paddy McKee!"

"I hope it's a sign of things to come and Mary won't be coming up here again. I'm getting too old for all this drama." Silver bids his mother-in-law good night and Mary, Anne and he, walk out and get into the car. As they are driving down the road Silver remembers that there isn't a bite to eat in the house and he asks Barney to stop at a shop on the way. Barney keeps driving and a few minutes later they arrive at Silver's house. As Silver is getting out he lifts Anne and the case as Barney and Mary are talking.

"There's not a bite in the house Barney. I thought you could have stopped at the shop so I could get some rations," says Silver. Barney walks to the back of the car and opens the boot and lifts out a large box.

"I think every thing you need will be in here; bacon, eggs, sausages, bread, milk and Farley's rusks for the child. Have I left anything out?"

"Jesus Barney, how can I thank you."

"I'll tell you how Paddy. Treat that woman and your child right and stay off the drink. That's all the thanks I would want." Tears run down Silver's cheeks but he quickly pulls out his handkerchief and blows his nose and wipes away the tears.

"No one is ever going to see him cry. Not now, not ever," Barney says, "and another thing Paddy, "forget about your pride. It will probably kill you. "

Barney gets in the car and drives off. As Silver opens the front door and lets Mary go in first. He carries in the rations and the case. When he comes in to the kitchen Mary is crying. She throws her arms around Silver and asks him, "Have I got my old Paddy back?"

"As far as I can promise you, I will do my best for us and that's all I can say. Would you like a cup of tea, Mary or will I make a fry?"

* * *

A few weeks later Silver is finding his new life a bit boring and asks Mary would she like a night out at the dogs. Mary tells him that she would rather sit at home and watch television and if he wants to go alone it's fine by her.

"Are you sure?" asks Silver. Mary replies that she would be fine and she is going to have a bath and that means the tin bath in front of the fire. So it would be better if he went out for a few hours. She asks Silver to carry the bath in and he duly obliges.

"Well Mary, I could change my mind and sit in and pour the water over your hair."

"You just go on about your business and I can pour the water over my own hair. I know what your thinking." Both laugh. Silver then grabs his coat and heads out. He is going to the dogs because it's a big night. It's the National Sprint tonight and everyone will be there. He walks down the street and meets two old friends; Skinny Reynolds and Frankie Quinn who are standing at the corner. Both greet him and show a little respect to him as they can see that he's back to himself. "Youse boys want to go to the dogs at Dunmore with me."

Skinny looks at Frankie and they reply in unison, "We're skint Paddy." "I didn't ask you, had you any money, I asked you did you want to go." "Yes I'd love to go," says Skinny.

"What about you?"

"No problem. I'd love to go but how do we get up there. It's a good bit away."

"I'm going to treat you well. We'll get a taxi out of Sally Rogers and I'll pay the ways in." Skinny and Frankie rub their hands. The three of them then walk around to Cromac Street and walk into the taxi depot and Silver orders a taxi. As the three of them get into the taxi the driver asks Silver is he doing ok as he hasn't seen him around lately.

"Doing all right, son. Just getting by, trying to get a bob or two."

"I suppose you don't remember me. I used to work for Silver cabs. I was the one brought you up to the Shankill the night you fought Stormy."

"That wasn't a fight. I was drunk as a skunk."

"I know I drove you up. I tried to talk you out of it but you wouldn't listen."

"Him and me are friends now and them days are over, I hope." The driver asks Silver can he ask him a question."Okay son, as long as it's not about fighting."

"There was a rumour in Silver cabs that it was called after you. You know what I mean, the Silver part."

"Look, if every yarn I've heard about me was true, for a start I'd be six foot tall and a millionaire and married about six times. Does that answer your question son?" As the taxi pulls up at Dunmore Park and the boys get out and Silver goes to the driver's window to pay him.

"This one is on me Silver. You know it's great to see you back to your old self again. I thought you where dead, honest to God I did. Silver tries in vain to pay the guy but he just drives off.

"You see Silver, you don't need money," says Skinny.

"Yeah, but its handy when your going to the shop. They're not interested if I'm Silver or yellow brass, it's the real world out there."

Frankie butts in, "you don't need money in the Market, Silver every shop keeper remembers the turns you done them."

"Hopefully my fighting days are over, I'm tired of this mantle of being a hard man. It's like a fifty pound weight around my neck and it's killing me." Skinny puts his finger at the side of his head and whispers to Frankie."I think he losing his marlies." As they walk into the betting arena of Dunmore, the crowd stop what they are doing and look at Silver. Within minutes they are queuing up to shake hands with him and congratulating him on how he looks. Silver is getting embarrassed and walks into the crowd and tries to mingle with everyone but its hard work. Most of the punters are back slapping him and greeting him. Then he spies Quinn who is making a book and he gets a bit irritated but tonight isn't the night to pull anyone. This is the biggest night of the year at the dogs and it wouldn't go down too well. Silver looks across the betting ring and spies Stormy coming out of the toilet and watches him as he walks in front of Quinn's pitch. Silver now knows that he is working for Quinn and accepts that he's not going to rock the boat and pick a fight with Stormy.

He's not ready for him nor does he want to fight in his head. He has retired.

The public address system announces that the dogs are parading for the final of the National Sprint and they have five minutes to place their bets. Quinn is going, "six to four the favourite" and there is a rush from the punters to get on. Quinn shouts that they will all get on, and he lays away in frenzy. As the dogs are going into the traps Quinn goes seven to four the favourite and there's another mad rush as everyone wants to back the favourite. Stormy is holding back the crowd, when a guy comes up behind Silver and whispers to him, "the favourite is a dead one. The second co is a certainty. Go in and help yourself." It's Banbridge John who is a good judge of a dog and hears most things that are going on. He along with some others from Banbridge. Dom Quinn, Blondie, big Dermy, and Chippy Joe and a few Newry men, one of whom, Brendan Matthews, is the owner of the second favourite, the best dog trainer in the country. John Knocker then walks over to Silver and asks him what John had said. As soon as Silver tells Knocker he runs over to Jimmy McQuaid another bookie and has a tenner on the second favourite and tells his mates Mark, Jackie, and Housty to help themselves. Silver tells Skinny and Frankie to stick close to him and to watch his back. Silver walks over to Quinn and asks for fifty pounds on the second favourite. Quinn asks Silver for the money which is unusual as you can call bets if you're well known and there's nobody better known than Silver in Belfast. Silver pulls out his money that he has saved since he went off the drink and goes to pay Quinn.

"No, you've no bet," says Quinn and Silver asks him why. "I don't have to tell you why you can't have a bet with me. Now fuck off!" The hare is running, is announced over the public address and the dogs are off. The favourite leads them up to the top bend but he wanders off towards the hare rail and a big outsider ironically called La Costa Nostra and owned by the McGuinness brothers gets up to win by four lengths. Quinn is rubbing his hands and Silver walks over to him and tells him never to embarrass him in front of people again or he will wring his neck.

Quinn tells Stormy to sort it out and turns his back on Silver and starts counting the money in his bag. Stormy tells Silver although it is good to see him, he's working for Quinn and would he move off and let them get on with making a book for the last race, invariably called The Lucky Last. Silver moves away and the crowd are in a hush. They have never seen Silver take a step back from anyone and the stories they heard are now just distant memories as Silver walks away with his head down followed by Skinny and Frankie. Silver finds a corner and he sits on a ledge and Skinny says to him. "I never thought I'd see the day."

"Me neither," says Frankie... "Silver lapping it". The public address system announces that the dogs are in the traps for the last race and the crowds leave the betting ring and run to see the last race. Silver stands up and gives his coat to Skinny and his money to Frankie to hold for him as he walks up to Stormy and asks him did he think he was talking to a mug. Stormy takes off his coat and squares up to Silver and punches him right flush on the chin. Quinn starts shouting the odds.

"You can have two to one McKee! Anyone want to take it! Let's be having you!" The crowds are now back in the arena after thirty seconds of The Lucky Last, five two five race and there is a lot of arguing among the crowd.

As Silver and Stormy punch away at each other some one from the crowd shouts, "Quinn got the favourite stopped in the big race!" Silver is now on top of Stormy and is about to deliver the coup de grace and he pulls back. The crowd is now baying for Quinn's blood.

Silver says to Stormy, "Do you still want to back that weasel up?" Silver draws his fist back and Stormy says, "No, I think your right about him. Silver gets off Stormy and lets him up and he walks straight over to Quinn and asks for his nights pay. As Quinn pays him, Stormy say, "never in your life do that with me again, them guys all working all week and your laying them a dead one, I've a good mind to break your neck myself'. Stormy walks over to Silver and shakes hands and the crowd roars with approval. Frankie and Skinny walk over and hands Silver his money and coat and Frankie says, "I told you Silver would never lap it".

"You must have a bad memory Frankie. I did know. He wouldn't because he never did in his life!" says Skinny.

Chapter 16

It's now coming up to Christmas and Silver still hasn't got a job as such but gets the odd day working at the docks, loading cows and sheep onto the boats but today he has to go to court. As he is lighting the fire, he grabs an old Irish News and rolls it up in a ball and places some sticks on it, then the coal. As he stacks the fire and lights it, he places a sheet of paper over the fire to get it going ,he hears the child crying and he shouts up the stairs to Mary... "Is everything all right up there?"

"No, the child is freezing and so am I."

"Well the fire is lit. Give it a few minutes and the kitchen will be warm. I will call you down in a few minutes". As Silver gets the fire going, he goes out to the scullery and puts the teapot on. It's the sixteenth of December and he has to go to court. Harry has promised him a few quid and all he has to do is follow whatever the barrister says. After a few minutes he calls Mary and the child down and hands Mary a cup off tea.

"Tell you what Mary, you and the child come around to the ITL about one o'clock and I will buy you a nice fry for your breakfast. I'm getting some money today and then we can go Christmas shopping."

"God that would be great Paddy. Can we go to the co-op? I love that shop and we can take Anne to see Father Christmas. Maybe get her a few things she needs; shoes and stockings and maybe a dolls pram would be nice. A tree for that corner there would definitely look nice and it would hide the dampness on that wall, because I'm sick looking at it."

"If I get what Harry promised me, I will buy you and Anne complete new outfits." How much did he promise you a thousand laughs Mary? No but he did promise me two hundred quid and that will look after us for a month or two. The court will probably be over about half twelve he said and I will come straight over to you in the café how does that sound. Yes it will give me time to do a few things around the house and get Anne dressed. Silver looks at the clock and its nine forty five and he tells Mary that he will head over to the court. Silver grabs his coat and heads out the door after giving Mary and Anne a peck on the cheek. Mary calls him back.

"Is there any chance you could get into trouble over this and finish in jail again?"

"No, Mary. The barrister explained to me this is what's called a civil action. I'm only a witness. If I thought there was any chance I could go back to Crumlin Road jail, there'd be no chance of me going to court today I'd run a mile. No chance what so ever." Silver closes the door and heads on down the street and makes his way to the courthouse. As he walks in Billy McCausland, looks at him in a wily way, and walks over to meet him.

"What have you to say for yourself Paddy?"

"Not a lot. Only to tell you I haven't forgotten you calling me sheep's head."

"I was drunk. Can you not forgive and forget?"

"I can forgive but in all honesty it's hard to forget." Billy sticks his hand out and Silver shakes it.

"Look Paddy, Harry and myself have come to an agreement over all this and the judge will give me my deeds back and I will owe him a thousand quid. You will get a few quid from Harry for doing the time and everyone will have a happy Christmas."

"Sounds a bit like a fairytale but as long as I get something I will be happy, or it will be a poor Christmas in our house."

"Here he is now. Let's hear what he has to say. Harry walks over to Silver and tells him to follow him into the toilet. Inside the toilet Harry hands him a large envelope and tells him not to be opening it until the court is over or they will all be arrested.

"How much is in it Harry?" asks Silver.

"I told you; two hundred quid and I'm a man of my word." Both men shake hands and walk back into the court halls. Silver presses his hand on his breast, checking the envelope, as it's all the money he has and it gives him a good feeling. He has the Christmas money now.

It's now ten thirty and the court intercom announces that number one court is now sitting.

The three men walk in together and take their seats in the courtroom.

"All rise," announces the clerk of the court as a stern old judge walks in and takes his seat. The judge fumbles about and reads some paper and asks both legal teams have they come to an agreement.

"There's just a few things to be ironed out and we need Your Worship's guidance and direction but it looks straight forward enough." The judge asks the other barrister if he is in agreement and he replies, "yes."

"So am I led to believe that both parties have agreed on terms, agreed by both your briefs?"

Harry's barrister gets up and asks the judge to release the money and deeds to both parties. It will be distributed to each party.

"Let me hear what both men have to say," requests the judge.

"We call Mister Harry Robinson to the stand." After Harry takes the oath the judge asks him to explain his side of the story.

"I lent Mister McCausland ten thousand pound against his title deeds to get him out of a bit of trouble and both are now wards of the court – the money and the deeds."

"So you acted as a moneylender in this escapade? Do you have a moneylender's licence?" Big Bob gets on his feet and explains to the judge that it was a loan between two friends. The judge then asks was there any interest involved or "lets say a sweetener?"

"No, Your Worship. It was a plain and simple loan between two friends where one gave his title deeds as a deposit just in case he didn't pay."

"Ah! I see a loan between two friends. Sounds a bit more like a loan with guarantees, would I be right in saying? Did anyone witness this arrangement?"

"Yes, Your Worship. Mr. McKee, "pointing down at Silver. Bob tells the judge that he is sitting in the court. The judge looks down at Silver and writes something on a sheet of paper. "Will there be any more questions from other parties?"

"No, Your Worship."

"That will be all then, Mister Robinson." Harry leaves the witness box and walks back to the body of the court. The clerk calls Billy McCausland. Billy takes the oath and settles down in the witness box. His barrister gets to his feet and outlines his client's case. The judge looks up and asks his counsel can he tell him why they are in court, if terms were agreed by both counsels' briefs.

"We need the money and the deeds released to our respective clients, Your Worship."

"I see and what exactly is Mister McKee doing here.?"

"Well, he witnessed the agreement on the day and he is here to give independent, collaborating evidence, without prejudice."

"I see."

Billy's barrister asks him to explain what happened on the day and after a few minutes the judge tells him that he can leave the stand. Bob then calls Patrick McKee to the stand. Silver takes the stand and the oath. Bob asks Silver to outline what happened on the day and Silver repeats literally verbatim what Harry and Billy have already said.

"So you where the last person with the money on the day and I see here, you went to jail for possession of counterfeit money and possession of ten thousand pounds." Silver replies meekly that he only went to jail for possession of the counterfeit money and..." nothing else your worship."

"I see. I'm going to adjourn until after lunch and have a read at the papers of this case. I will give my decision when I come back but it looks straight forward enough. By the way Mister McKee, do you have a bank account?"

"No Your Worship. Why?"

"I just would like to see if there has been any change of large amounts of money going in or out of your account."

"Your Worship, I have never had a bank account."

"Well everyone should have a bank account. Makes you more careful about how you spend your money."

"I've never had that problem, Sir."

"So we shall adjourn?"

"All rise," says the clerk and they all get on their feet as the judge walks out. Silver, Harry and Billy walk out into the court halls and have a discussion with both barristers.

"I thought this would be a formality. Why did he adjourn?"

"It's normal practice. He doesn't want to start another case, so it covers the day nicely." Silver asks the time and Harry tells him it's a quarter past twelve. Silver tells them he has to go and asks does he have to come back in the afternoon. Bob tells him to come back at two o'clock but that it will only take about ten minutes and he will be away again before two thirty.

"No problem. I'm off to meet the wife. Silver walks out of the court and Harry and Billy look at him as he walks down the chambers.

"I hope he doesn't open that envelope," says Harry. "You should have told him he didn't have to come back." Bob calls Silver back and tells him that he doesn't really have to come back.

It's entirely up to himself.

Silver walks across the street and into the ITL café where Mary and Anne are sitting. Mary is drinking a cup of tea and feeding the child some ice cream as Silver walks up to the counter and orders two large fries with two eggs on his, and a fresh pot of tea for two. As he sits down Mary asked him how it went and he tells her that he has to go back to court but he will only be away for ten minutes, so she can sit and wait on him here.

"I'm really just going over to see how they will work it all out."

"Did you get the money?"

"Yes. I have it in my inside pocket. Here you mind it for me. I shouldn't be carrying it with me when I go back to the court." After eating his fry Silver drinks his tea and gets up and pays the bill and tells Mary he won't be long. As he walks over to the court he meets Harry who asks him has he got the envelope and Silver tells him his wife has it for safe keeping.

"That's good. So you didn't open it?"

"No. I just gave it to Mary and told her to hold it until I came out of court. I didn't want anyone to see it, especially the judge."

"That was smart now its time to get in and get this wrapped up." All three walk into the court and take their seats and go through the ritual, all rise and the court begins.

The judge says that after reading the papers he has made a ruling.

"In my opinion, this is a case tainted with lies and innuendo. The only thing that stands out, is the fact that Mister McCausland owns the title deeds and I make a judgment that they are returned to him. Now we get down to the money. It seems that Mister McKee was arrested in possession of both the counterfeit money and for want of a better term the real money or legal tender. On the day there was confusion as to who owned the money but not until Mister McKee was charged with having counterfeit money. Now in my eyes if Mister McKee wasn't charged with having stolen money in regards to the ten thousand pounds, one has to wonder who owned the money." Billy looks at Harry and Silver and Harry mouths, 'I will kill you if I don't get this money back, Billy.' The judge then makes his final summing up.

"I am going to award the ten thousand pounds to the man who had it in his possession when arrested by the police. I note they didn't charge him with theft or even ask him where he got it. So as the law stands I award the ten thousand pounds to Mister McKee and that's my decision. The court will now rise."

Harry looks at Silver and asks, "you will give it back to me and I will look after you Paddy."

"Yes, that would be the decent thing to do Harry. When I get it I will let you know and I will hand it over to you."

"Good man Paddy I knew you would do the right thing."

Billy walks over to both men and says; "I've never heard a decision like that in my life." The two barristers come over both shaking their heads.

"I think he got it all wrong but he has the final say. It can't go any further other than to the House of Lords. And that would cost a fortune."

"It's all right. Paddy has agreed to reimburse me when he gets the money. So we're all happy." The three men shake hands and depart and Silver makes his way over to the ITL to meet Anne and Mary. As he walks in he nods to Mary to get her bag and follow him and they will dander down to the co-op a large shop in the city centre. On arrival at the co-op Silver asks Mary for the envelope and tells her that he was awarded the ten thousand pounds but he agreed to give it back to Harry when he gets it. After all it belongs to him and he has been fair with him. They first go in to the grotto to see Father Christmas and Silver is enjoying himself like a big child. They then walk to the ladies fashion desk and Mary buys a few things and Silver opens the envelope to pay the lady who is actually a friend and neighbour of his and comes from the market. As he hands her a twenty pound note the woman goes to the till and is looking at a piece of paper and suddenly turns red.

"Have you any more money on you Paddy?"

" Why what's wrong with that note? It's on a list we have here. It's counterfeit and if I were you I'd get rid of it quickly knowing your record."

"I haven't any more money Trish."

"Look Paddy, just leave the items on the counter. I will make it look normal but if I was you I would walk over to that toilet and flush that note away. Just in case the police come in and search you. One never knows." Silver danders over to the toilet and walks in and locks the door behind him. As he fumbles with the money and checks it, he sees that they all have the same number. He starts tearing them up into little pieces and flushes them down the toilet. He moves from toilet to toilet to get it done in a hurry in case he is caught because that would mean a big sentence in jail. Silver walks out of the toilet and over to the counter where Mary is standing with Anne and Trish and they are pretending that Mary has lost her purse.

"Lets get out of here Mary, and thanks Trish, you're a darling."

"Can't have a Market man going to jail can we?" Silver and Mary walk out and up the street towards home. Silver is cursing Harry and everyone belonging to him. As he turns into his street he sees a squad car sitting adjacent to his house, so he warns Mary to say nothing. As they open the hall door the police get out of the car and tell Silver that he is under arrest for being in possession of counterfeit money.

"If you like, we can come in and search you here and get it all over and done with or the whole family can come down to the station."

Silver and Mary both agree to being searched and after an hour or so the police apologise to Mary and Silver and tell him they where acting on good information.

"Yes, I know the kind of information you were acting on. That person always takes insurance out and backs himself back, in all his dealing."

"I don't know what you mean Sir."

"I didn't think you would. Very few people would." The cops leave Silver's house and Mary says she didn't think that, that was a nice thing to do in the mouth of Christmas. Mary sits down and starts to cry.

"Don't be crying Mary. I'm keeping the ten thousand the court awarded me. Them two bastards thought they where smart. Just too smart for their own good." Silver laughs.

On the twenty third of December, Silver is standing in the same court where the judge awarded him the money. "I told you to get a bank account Mister McKee. I wasn't kidding. Here is a cheque for ten thousand pounds. Take care of it and yourself. I think you were used and abused by two people who just thought they were smart."

The judge winks at Silver and as he takes off his wig, Silver looks at him as he winks his eye. He is the very man that Silver has had a nodding acquaintance with and has seen him on many occasions on Fridays in the variety Markets. Silver puts the cheque in his pocket and walks out of the court where Mary and Anne are waiting on him. He pulls the check out and waves it at Mary.

"We're rich Mary, more money than I ever had in my life. Let's go home." As they are walking over the bridge Silver takes a half crown from his pocket and shows it to Mary. He throws it from the bridge and it skims across the water and sinks.

"Why did you do that Paddy? That's the end of Silver McKee. It's now simple Patrick Joseph McKee. He grabs Mary and kisses her and says, "and I love you Mary and my daughter Anne."

Both walk hand in hand with baby Anne, her first wee steps with her proud parents, across the bridge.